BOBBS-MERRILL

Best of Children's Literature

The books in this series are:

SUNNY AND GAY

FOOLISH AND WISE

FUN ALL AROUND

SHINING HOURS

TIME FOR ADVENTURE

BEYOND THE HORIZON

LIBRARY OF CONGRESS CATALOG CARD NUMBER: 60-12936

SHINING HOURS

SHINING HOURS

Bobbs·Merrill

Best of Children's Literature

Compilers and Editors

NILA BANTON SMITH
Director, Reading Institute
New York University

HAZEL C. HART
Assistant Professor of Education
Butler University

CLARA BELLE BAKER
Former Director, Children's School
National College of Education

THE **BOBBS-MERRILL** COMPANY, INC.
A SUBSIDIARY OF HOWARD W. SAMS & CO., INC.
Publishers · INDIANAPOLIS · NEW YORK

SHINING HOURS

CONTENTS

REACHING UP

WOULD YOU BELIEVE?

LOOKING AROUND YOU

THE WORLD'S CHILDREN

STORYLAND TRAILS

READ FOR FUN

"It was really very strange," said Uncle Fritz thoughtfully. "Someone must have left the hat by mistake."

Without saying anything, Ted and Jean sat down at once to listen. They knew that their uncle was getting ready to tell a story, and they didn't want to miss a word of it.

Uncle Fritz leaned back comfortably in his big chair and began the story.

"One noon I had lunch with some friends," he said. "When it was time to leave, I went to get my hat. I was surprised to find that the only hat left wasn't mine."

"Somebody had taken your hat by mistake," guessed Jean.

Uncle Fritz nodded. "That's what I thought, so I took the left-over hat even though it was most unusual looking. It was green, very hairy, and an inch wider than most hats."

"Could you wear it?" asked Ted.

"Yes, but I wondered how anyone could have mistaken my old brown hat for that odd green one," answered Uncle Fritz.

"I walked several blocks," he went on, "before I remembered that I hadn't worn a hat to lunch. My old brown hat was at home."

The children chuckled but said nothing.

"Such a silly mistake made me feel pretty foolish," said Uncle Fritz. "The only thing I could do, of course, was turn around right away and take the hat back.

"Soon I met a lady, and I tipped the hat politely. The lady screamed and ran away as fast as she could go."

"Why did she do that?" asked Jean.

"That's exactly what I asked myself," said Uncle Fritz. "The green hat was in my right

hand, so I put my left hand up to find out whether something was wrong with my hair or with the top of my head."

"Was anything wrong?" asked Ted.

"Not exactly wrong," answered Uncle Fritz carelessly, "but perhaps sort of queer. You see, a live rabbit was sitting there."

Both children gasped, but Uncle Fritz went right on. "I put the rabbit down, and it ran away. Then I put the hat back on and walked along. I noticed that everybody I met looked at me very queerly, though."

Ted just couldn't keep quiet. "Was there another rabbit?" he asked.

Uncle Fritz shook his head. "I looked at myself in a big window," he said, "and there wasn't any rabbit. The hat was there, all right, but I wasn't exactly wearing it. Instead, it was floating in the air, a few inches above my head."

Jean and Ted laughed as they pictured the hat floating above their uncle's head.

"I reached up to pull the hat down," Uncle Fritz went on. "I pulled with both hands, but it wouldn't come down. By this time a small crowd was watching me.

"I tried to pretend that nothing unusual was happening, but I walked faster. The hat kept coming, too, floating along in the air, several inches above my head.

"I tried walking on tiptoe, but that didn't work. My head didn't quite reach the hat, and my toes soon got tired.

"Next I tried pretending that I had to tie my shoe. I bent over. Down came the hat, but it stopped several inches above my head. I straightened up suddenly. It worked! My head went into the hat clear to my ears!"

The children clapped, and Uncle Fritz made a funny little bow.

"I was really proud of myself," he smiled, "but I didn't want the hat any longer. For a moment I quite forgot that it wasn't mine, and I threw it as far as I could."

Ted was afraid that was the end of the hat and the end of the story, but it wasn't.

"Just when I thought that I had seen the last of the hat," Uncle Fritz went on, "two

pigeons flew out of it. The next thing I knew, those two pigeons had brought the hat back and put it on my head again."

Ted thought of the way the hat had floated above his uncle's head before. "Did the hat stay on this time?" he asked.

"I didn't give it a chance," Uncle Fritz answered. "I held it tightly under one arm and hurried along."

"What happened next?" asked Jean.

"I stopped at the street corner for a red light," said Uncle Fritz. "As I stood there, waiting, a policeman tapped my shoulder and told me I was losing something.

"I looked back and saw a piece of blue silk cloth trailing on the sidewalk."

"It was coming out of the hat, wasn't it?" asked Ted, laughing.

"That's right," nodded Uncle Fritz. "The policeman bent over to pick it up, and as he did so, he pulled it.

"The blue piece of silk cloth was tied to a long, red piece, which was tied to a long, yellow piece. The yellow piece of silk cloth was tied to an orange piece, and that was tied to a bright purple piece."

13

"Did the policeman think you were playing a trick on him?" asked Jean.

"I'm afraid he did," said Uncle Fritz. "He kept on pulling, and his face got redder and redder. I could see that he was angry, so I tried to explain about the hat.

"I held it out for the policeman to see, but the strangest thing had happened. The hat had turned into a live duck!"

The children gasped, and Uncle Fritz had to laugh at their surprise.

"That duck flapped itself right out of my hands," he went on. "It ran into the street, quacking and flapping. The policeman started to chase it, and I went home."

Uncle Fritz stopped.

"What about the hat?" asked Ted.

"Oh, it belonged to a man who did magic acts on the stage," said Uncle Fritz.

"Did he ever get it back?" Jean asked.

"Yes, the hat went home by itself," said Uncle Fritz. "The man had trained it—best trained hat I ever have seen, too."

"How can you train a hat?" asked Ted.

"It isn't easy," said Uncle Fritz. "You must start when it's a very small cap!"

14

FATS TAKES THE CAKE

Billy had been invited to Stew's birthday party, but Fats hadn't.

"Maybe Stew made a mistake and forgot to invite you," said Billy.

"Maybe he didn't," Fats replied. "I had a big fight with him last week."

"Why did you do that?" demanded Billy. "I should think you could have remembered when his birthday is. He always has a party on his birthday."

Fats didn't say anything, so Billy asked, "Why don't you go and make up with him?"

"How can I?" demanded Fats. "I don't even remember what the fight was about."

"That doesn't matter," said Billy. "Just go around and say that you were wrong."

"I will not!" shouted Fats. "I was right, and Stew can come around and make up with me if he wants me at his old party!"

Billy gave up and went home.

The party turned out to be a treasure hunt, the kind where everybody has to find all the things on a list. Not even Stew knew ahead of time what was on the list.

First each boy had to draw a girl's name out of a hat, to see who his partner would be. Billy drew Peggy's name. Stew drew a blank slip, because at the last minute one of the girls hadn't been able to come. That meant Stew had to go without a partner.

Stew's mother said there would be a prize for the partners who found everything and came back to the front porch first. Then she handed the same list to each two partners:

pine cone
1924 penny
garden rake
last Sunday's paper
sock with a hole in it
black cat

Almost everybody rushed off and started to ring doorbells.

"Hurry up," exclaimed Peggy. "They're all getting ahead of us."

Billy stood still and looked at the list. "The only thing hard to find will be that black cat," he said. Then he happened to remember something. "Come on," he cried.

He cut through a few yards and rushed up the street to see whether Fats was home.

16

Fats was there, all right, sitting on the front steps. "What's the matter?" he asked. "Did you have a fight with Stew, too?"

"No, it's a treasure hunt, and I have to find a black cat," explained Billy.

"Well, start finding," said Fats, "and hurry, because here comes Peggy."

"You wait for me, Billy," Peggy panted. "Partners are supposed to stay together."

"Then keep up with me," said Billy. "Now listen, Fats. Last spring your little brother Bobby gave me a black kitten, but my mother wouldn't let me keep it."

"I know," said Fats. "Our mother wouldn't let us keep it, either."

"Well, where is it now?" asked Billy.

"How should I know?" asked Fats. "Bobby gave it away. I don't know who took it."

"Ask him, can't you?" begged Billy.

"I don't even know where he is," said Fats. "He went somewhere to play, and he doesn't have to be back until suppertime."

"Suppertime!" exclaimed Billy. "I need a black cat before suppertime. Find Bobby and ask him, will you? Please! Then you could get the cat and have it here by the time I come back with the other things."

"Why should I?" asked Fats. "I wasn't even invited to this old party."

"Listen, Fats," said Billy. "If you get me that cat, I'll bring you some cake."

"They'll have ice cream, too," said Fats.

"I'll bring everything," promised Billy.

"Well, all right," Fats agreed, and he got up slowly and went to look for Bobby.

"See, we're doing it the smart way," Billy pointed out to Peggy. "Now all we have to do is dig up the other things and pick up our cat on the way back."

18

"*If* Fats gets the cat," sniffed Peggy.

"What do you mean, *if?* I can count on good old Fats," said Billy.

They found a pine cone at once. Then they rang doorbells and asked for all the other things. By the end of one block, they had the sock with a hole in it, last Sunday's paper, and the rake. The only thing they had to promise to return was the rake.

Then they started on the next block, still looking for a 1924 penny. When Billy rang the bell at one house, a little old lady came to the door to see what he wanted.

19

"We're on a treasure hunt," Billy began, "and we want to ask——"

"What? What?" said the little old lady. "Speak up. I'm a little hard of hearing."

"A treasure hunt!" shouted Billy. The old lady never had heard of such a thing, and it took Billy a long time to explain what one was. Finally the old lady got the idea.

"How exciting!" she cried. "A 1924 penny. Why, I have a whole jar of pennies in the kitchen. Wait, I'll get it."

She brought the jar, and they started to look at the pennies, one at a time.

"1924!" shouted Billy, finally, holding up the penny. The old lady was almost as excited as he was about the penny.

Billy put the 1924 penny in his pocket with the sock and the pine cone. Then he picked up the rake and dashed away to find Fats. Peggy followed with the Sunday paper, screaming, "Wait, wait!"

Fats was nowhere to be seen, so Billy ran up the steps and banged on the screen door. In a minute, Bobby came to the door.

"Where's Fats?" Billy asked.

"He's not here," said Bobby.

"What!" exclaimed Billy.

"I told you so," said Peggy.

"If you came for the black cat, I have it in here," said Bobby. "Fats told me to give it to you. Wait a minute."

He got the cat and gave it to Billy.

"Good old Fats," said Billy, petting the cat. "Now let's not waste any more time. You take the rake, Peggy, and let's get back to Stew's house as fast as we can."

They were almost to Stew's house when they saw several pairs of partners coming from the other direction. "Hurry," cried Billy.

He and Peggy put on a final burst of speed and skimmed up the steps ahead of the others.

The porch was crowded and noisy. Partners were still returning, and Stew's mother was trying to count what they had brought back. The cats were trying to start fights with each other. Billy was loudly pointing out that his cat was the blackest of all.

Finally Stew's mother got things quieted down enough to say, "Return the borrowed things and hurry back. Then we'll have ice cream and cake and give out the prize."

Several boys shouted, "Who won?"

Billy had his mouth open to say that he and Peggy had won, when he noticed Fats in a far corner of the porch.

"Say, what are *you* doing here," he called. "You weren't invited."

"He was, too," said Stew, stepping over to Fats. "He's my partner, and we won."

"What!" shouted Billy.

"Sure," said Stew. "I had everything but the cat when I happened to see Fats. He just happened to have a black cat, so I invited him to be my partner."

"What black cat?" asked Billy.

"They had one, all right," Stew's mother said, "but they've already returned it."

"Yes," Fats spoke up. "I hurried right home with it, and I told Bobby not to give it to anyone but you."

"Why, you—you—that was *my* cat," howled Billy. "It was my idea to get it."

"Well, you got it, didn't you? Wasn't it there waiting for you?" asked Fats. "Look, I won't even make you keep your part of the bargain. You don't have to bring me any ice cream or cake."

"I should say I don't!" shouted Billy.

"As long as I'm here anyway, I can get my own," said Fats happily.

ELETELEPHONY

Once there was an elephant,
Who tried to use the telephant—
No! No! I mean an elephone
Who tried to use the telephone—
(Dear me! I am not certain quite
That even now I've got it right.)

Howe'er it was, he got his trunk
Entangled in the telephunk;
The more he tried to get it free,
The louder buzzed the telephee—
(I fear I'd better drop the song
Of elephop and telephong!)

From *Tirra Lirra* by Laura E. Richards. Reprinted by permission of Little, Brown & Co.

JENNY AND HER PETS

It was hot and crowded inside the elephant tent. In the distance, you could hear circus men shouting, "Pea—nuts! Pop—corn! You can't make friends with the elephants if you don't have Pea—nuts! Pop—corn!"

The long line of elephants swayed slowly, with their trunks skimming the ground and their great ears fanning backward and forward. Clank-clankety-clank went the heavy iron chains that were fastened to one foot of each elephant.

A boy pushed his way to the front of the crowd. He was watching the elephant at one end of the line. That is, he was watching the dog stretched out asleep beside the elephant. The little dog's head was resting comfortably on the elephant's big white-washed foot.

"Say, Mister," the boy finally said to the keeper who sat near by. "Won't that elephant step on the little dog?"

"No, indeed. Don't worry!" the keeper said. This was Uncle Jed Tompkins who had taken care of the elephants for years. "Jenny won't hurt that pup one bit."

The boy watched then, as the elephant named Jenny gathered up some hay in her trunk and gently piled it on the top of the dog. "Why is she covering him up?" the boy asked. "He won't be able to breathe."

"Oh, yes, he will," Uncle Jed said. "Jenny covers him up for safekeeping until she gets back from doing her act in the ring." The boy was flabbergasted! He kept watching Jenny and the dog. After a while he asked whether the dog belonged to Uncle Jed.

The man chuckled. "Why, that's *her* dog, son," he answered with a smile.

"You're fooling me, Mister."

"I'm not fooling you," said Uncle Jed. "That elephant is crazy about pets. Worse than a boy like you, she is. And not only that—" Uncle Jed lowered his voice. "*All* the animals are crazy about Jenny, even the lions and tigers."

Just then the band struck up a march, and the old man got up. It was time for his elephants to go to the main tent. Uncle Jed threw a silk blanket over Jenny's back. The boy watched as she made ready to join the other elephants.

26

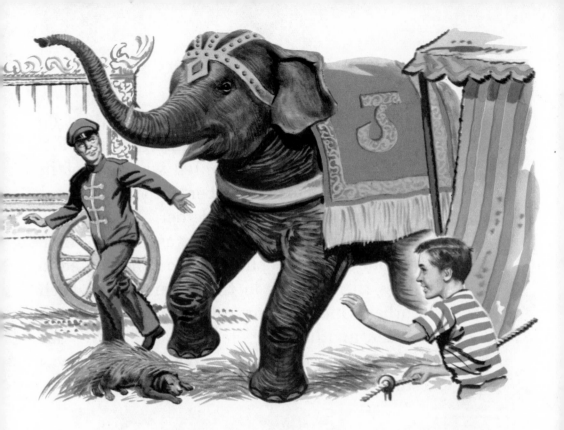

Gingerly, she pulled her front foot out from under the dog's head. Then she stepped away so carefully that she did not disturb the dog sleeping under the hay.

Everything went well until about two years later, when the little dog died. That was a real blow to Jenny. Until then, no one had realized how much the dog had meant to her.

Now, for days and days, Jenny stood with her head bowed and the end of her trunk touching the ground. She refused to eat and took almost no interest in things around her.

The circus people knew they had to do something to get Jenny's mind off the dog. So, even though Uncle Jed was against it, they decided to bring Albert into the elephant tent and chain him beside her. Albert was a killer elephant. Everyone was afraid of him.

One day the elephants in the line started to toss their trunks in the air and bump each other. One elephant trumpeted long and loud. Then another did. Jenny didn't move, but Uncle Jed rose from his stool to see what was making all the trouble.

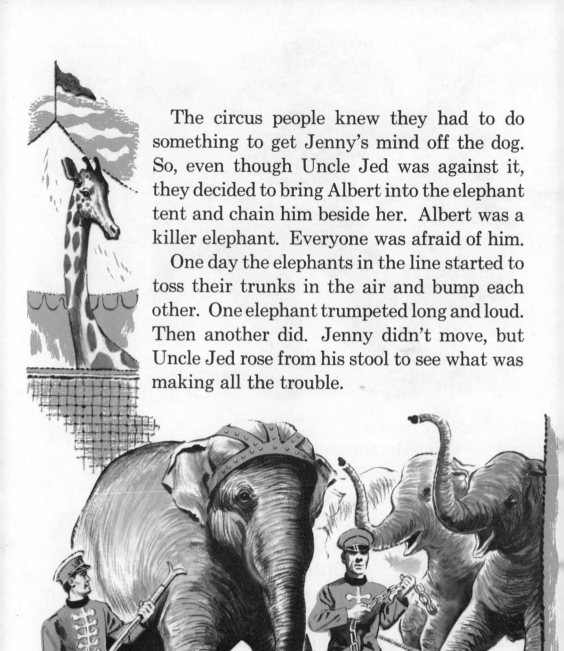

Albert was coming down the line. Two keepers walked beside him, carrying big clubs. Albert's feet were chained, and the heavy chains clanked as they dragged along.

The bad elephant was led into place beside Jenny. His big feet were chained to stakes. Circus workers gathered around, just close enough so they could help Jenny if she needed any kind of help.

The other elephants stamped their feet and tossed their trunks. Albert just stood there. He didn't trumpet or stamp or bump the others. He'd never been so quiet.

In a minute, Jenny perked up and began to take an interest in her new neighbor. Her tiny eyes looked him over. Then, all at once, her trunk reached over and fearlessly rested on the top of his head.

Albert swayed. His ears fanned. Now the men waited, ready to swing their clubs and hooks. Albert's trunk went up in the air as if to strike out. Then, gently, it caught hold of Jenny's trunk as though shaking hands.

"Well, I never!" cried Uncle Jed Tompkins. "That's just like her. Jenny's made a friend of mean old Albert!"

29

As the circus traveled around, Albert and
Jenny became fast friends. They were always
together, and Albert became much easier to
handle. He even learned to act in the ring. He
was still headstrong, however, and likely to
become angry over any little thing.

One summer, on a very hot day, the circus
was playing in a little town. The main tent
was packed with people, and the crowd was
watching eagerly as the sixty-five trained elephants went through their act.

All at once an elephant screamed. The
scream could be heard all over the circus lot.
It was Albert, angry over some little thing
that had happened. He screamed again, then
plunged down the circus track.

People yelled and ran as the huge, bellowing beast, blind with anger, came toward
them. The other elephants became frightened
and tried to break out of the ring. Circus
workers came from everywhere with clubs
and hooks.

Then, out of the crowd, came Jenny! Down
the track she thundered straight after Albert.
She drove herself between Albert and the
frightened people in the stands.

Wham! Wham! Her powerful trunk beat down on Albert's head as she pushed him away from the people. Albert was shaking from her blows, but he didn't fight back. Finally, Jenny turned him around. He grabbed her tail with his trunk, and they slowly lumbered away. No one ever called Albert a killer elephant again.

Several years later, Uncle Jed found Jenny

standing over Albert's lifeless body. She kept raising her trunk and trumpeting for someone to come and help him, but he couldn't be helped. He had died very suddenly.

Then began a battle to save Jenny's life. Again she wouldn't eat or take an interest in anything around her. She would stand for hours, her tiny eyes staring off into space. Albert had been such a care to her, and now she missed him too much to want to live.

Uncle Jed watched over her failing strength and couldn't do a thing about it. Another elephant was brought to her. A pony! A dog! A cat! None of them interested poor Jenny.

One day the circus unloaded at the edge of a new town. Jenny and all the other elephants were plodding along to the circus lot when they passed a field. Suddenly Jenny stopped. The elephant behind her and those down the line stopped. Uncle Jed tried to get her to move on, but she paid no attention.

The whole circus parade was at a standstill. Then Jenny stepped quietly out of line and started across the field. Uncle Jed yelled at her, but she didn't hear him. She just kept going faster all the time.

There in the center of the field, tied to a stake, was a black-and-white nanny goat. Jenny headed straight toward her, making soft, happy sounds through her trunk. The nanny goat looked up. She was surprised to see such a huge and strange-looking visitor, but she stood her ground and didn't move.

They met, those two, right out in the center of the field. For a few minutes they stood facing each other, as if talking things over. Then Jenny reached down and pulled the goat's stake clear out of the ground. She hurried the nanny goat across the field, and they fell in behind the parade.

Uncle Jed had to buy the nanny goat from the boy who owned her, but it was worth the money. Jenny was happy again. The boy and Uncle Jed sat down together outside the elephant tent after they had made the sale. The boy was puzzled.

"I'd like to know why she stole my goat," the boy said. "Of course, you paid me for it, but I can't understand why an elephant wants a little nanny goat."

Then he listened, wide eyed, while Uncle Jed told him about Jenny and her pets.

SUDDEN MARY

Once there was a little girl named Mary. She was a very sudden little girl. She was sudden when she tripped over the rugs. She was sudden when she fell off the fence into her father's flower beds. "I just could not stop," she would say.

She was sudden when she carried a plate of cookies into the dining room. "Why, where are the cookies?" she would say when she put the empty plate on the table.

She was sudden from early in the morning until she went to bed at night. She was sud-

Reprinted from *Till Potatoes Grow on Trees* by Emma L. Brock, by permission of Alfred A. Knopf, Inc.

den from Monday to Tuesday, and on through the week until Monday came around again.

Mary's mother kept busy wondering what Mary would do next. Her father gave her pennies for being careful not to fall into his flower beds. Her grandmother said Mary was as lively as a very lively goat and no safer. That is how sudden Mary was.

Just one person liked Mary's suddenness, and that person was her little sister. Little Sister was one quarter of the way from one year old to two years old. She could just barely walk on her short fat legs.

Every time that Mary fell over a footstool or tipped over a glass of milk, Little Sister would clap her hands and shout. She did not mind how sudden Mary was.

One Saturday morning in the wintertime, Mary thought she would like to visit Grandmother on the other side of town. It had snowed all the night before, and the snow was thick and soft. In some places it was very, very deep.

"I could take Little Sister," said Mary.

So Mary put on her snowsuit and her cap. She put on her overshoes and pulled on her

mittens. Little Sister had a snowsuit, too. When she was in it, she was just as wide as she was tall. When she tried to walk, she sat down.

Mother put Little Sister on the sled, and showed her how to hold on to the sides. Then she said, "Take your time, Mary. There is the whole morning to get there." Her mother knew how sudden Mary was.

"I hope Grandmother is baking some sugar cookies," Mary said as she started away.

Mary walked slowly and carefully along the walk, pulling Little Sister on the sled behind her. She scuffed through the snow and kicked clouds of it high in the air.

Mary made believe she was a horse. She snorted and stamped. She pranced right into the middle of old Mrs. Whittleby, who was coming along the walk.

Mrs. Whittleby's pocketbook flew out of her hand and made a hole in the snow. A package flew out of her other hand and made another hole in the snow. Mrs. Whittleby flew in still another direction and made a third and much larger hole in the snow. That is how sudden Mary was.

36

While Mrs. Whittleby was doing all that, Mary bounced back into Little Sister's lap. Little Sister laughed and laughed. She didn't care how sudden Mary was.

Mary picked herself up. She picked up the pocketbook and the package. Then she helped Mrs. Whittleby pick herself up. "I don't know how all that happened," said Mary.

Mary walked slowly and carefully along the walk, pulling Little Sister on the sled behind her. She scuffed through the snow and kicked clouds of it high in the air.

37

She came to a little hill where children had been coasting. The snow was hard and slippery as ice.

Mary made believe she was skating. She made believe so hard that her feet flew up in the air. The sled slid right past her and carried Little Sister down the hill alone.

The sled slid toward Mr. Tinkham's grocery store. It spilled Little Sister out into the snow and slid right into the store. That is how sudden Mary was.

Little Sister laughed and laughed. She did not care how sudden Mary was.

Mary walked slowly and carefully along the walk, pulling Little Sister on the sled behind her. She scuffed through the snow and kicked clouds of it high in the air.

Mary made believe that Grandmother was making sugar cookies. The more she thought of sugar cookies, the faster she went. She ran along the walk. She whirled around the schoolhouse corner. She whirled around another corner and up the path to Grandmother's house.

"Grandmother," she called. Grandmother came to the front door.

"Here I am, Grandmother," Mary shouted. "Here I am with Little Sister." Mary ran up to the front steps and pulled the sled up beside her. The sled was empty! There was no Little Sister. That is how sudden Mary was.

"Why, where is Little Sister?" cried Mary.

"Was she on the sled?" asked Grandmother.

"Well, she once was on the sled," said Mary.

Grandmother hurried into the house to put on her coat and overshoes. Mary ran down the path, pulling the empty sled behind her. She whirled around the corner onto the sidewalk. There was no Little Sister anywhere.

"Have you seen my little sister?" she asked Jimmy Green, who was pounding up a snowman in his front yard.

"No," said Jimmy Green. "There was nothing on your sled when you passed here."

Mary ran on toward the schoolhouse. There was no Little Sister anywhere.

"Have you seen my little sister?" Mary asked the school janitor, who was brushing snow off the schoolhouse steps.

"No, little girl," said the janitor. "Have you lost her somewhere?"

"Yes, she was on this sled," said Mary.

Then Mary saw people running. Mr. Tinkham was running from his grocery store, and Mr. Murphy, the big policeman, was running from across the street.

Mary looked at the spot toward which they were running. There she saw something waving from a snowbank. Sticking out of the snowbank were two fat brown overshoes, fastened to two fat blue snowsuit legs. The legs were kicking around in the air.

There was no sign of anything more. There was no sign of a face or mittens or a cap—just two legs kicking out of the snowbank.

Mary and Mr. Tinkham and Mr. Murphy rushed up to the waving legs. Mr. Murphy took hold of them and pulled hard. Out of the snowbank came the rest of Little Sister.

Little Sister was covered with snow, but she was laughing. She was laughing so hard that she couldn't stand on her fat legs.

"How ever did you get into the snowbank?" Mary asked her.

Mr. Tinkham brushed Little Sister off, and Mr. Murphy wiped her face with a handkerchief. Little Sister couldn't stop laughing. She did not care how sudden Mary was.

Then Grandmother came along and thanked the men who had brushed off Little Sister and wiped her face. Grandmother put Little Sister back on the sled. Then she pulled it safely around the corner to her house, where warm sugar cookies were waiting.

Grandmother said Mary was livelier than the very liveliest goat and much less safe. Mary's mother wondered what she would do next. Her father said that if Little Sister should be at all like Mary, he would never have any pennies for himself.

That is how sudden Mary was.

41

WYNKEN, BLYNKEN AND NOD

Wynken, Blynken, and Nod one night
   Sailed off in a wooden shoe—
Sailed on a river of crystal light,
   Into a sea of dew.
"Where are you going, and what do you
    wish?"
The old moon asked the three.
"We have come to fish for the herring fish
   That live in this beautiful sea;
   Nets of silver and gold have we!"
   Said Wynken, Blynken, and Nod.

The old moon laughed and sang a song,
   As they rocked in the wooden shoe;
And the wind that sped them all night long
   Ruffled the waves of dew.
The little stars were the herring fish
   That lived in that beautiful sea.
"Now cast your nets wherever you wish—
   Never afeared are we!"
So cried the stars to the fishermen three:
Wynken, Blynken, and Nod.

42

All night long their nets they threw
   To the stars in the twinkling foam—
Then down from the skies came the wooden
      shoe,
   Bringing the fishermen home.
'Twas all so pretty a sail, it seemed
   As if it could not be,
And some folk thought 'twas a dream
      they'd dreamed
   Of sailing that beautiful sea;
   But I shall name you the fishermen
      three:
   Wynken, Blynken, and Nod.

Wynken and Blynken are two little eyes,
   And Nod is a little head,
And the wooden shoe that sailed the skies
   Is a wee one's trundle-bed.
So shut your eyes while Mother sings
   Of wonderful sights that be,
And you shall see the beautiful things
   As you rock on the misty sea,
   Where the old shoe rocked the fishermen
      three:
   Wynken, Blynken, and Nod.

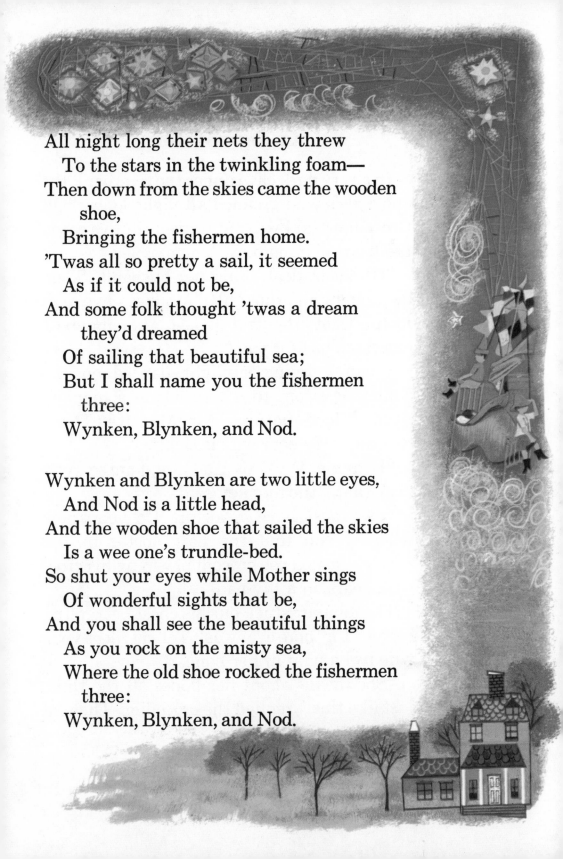

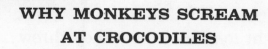

WHY MONKEYS SCREAM
AT CROCODILES

In a very dark cave under the riverbank the crocodile's wife groaned all night long. "Dr. Crocodile said I will not be well till I've eaten the heart of a monkey," she moaned.

"Oh, dear, dear," said her husband. Then he thought and thought. "Monkeys live high in the trees," he said at last, "but maybe I can catch one for you."

When morning sunlight danced on the water, he swam to a tree where a monkey lived. "Good morning, Mr. Mon Key Dee!" he said. "My poor wife is sick!"

"Dear me, Mr. Crok Ka Dilly, I am sorry to hear that," the monkey said.

"She must have a doctor. Do you know where I can find the best doctor in the jungle?" asked the crocodile, wiping his crocodile tears on a lily pad.

The monkey stuck out his chest. "I am the best doctor there ever was! Tell me, does your wife feel a pain in her bones?"

"She moans about her bones all the time, just like this!" replied the crocodile. Then he gave such a loud moan that it almost blew the monkey out of the tree.

"Just as I thought," said the monkey. "There has been much rain. Bones often hurt in damp weather. Of course, the river is damp, too."

The crocodile felt the water. "It is rather wet," he agreed.

Looking very important, the monkey swung down to the lowest branch on the tree. "My advice is that you move away from the river. No one is so dirty that he needs to take a hundred baths a day, as you crocodiles do."

"You are very wise," replied the crocodile. "If you will come to see my wife, Mr. Mon Key Dee, you can make her well!"

This pleased the proud monkey.

"Of course I can make her well!" he bragged. "The price will be ten bananas."

The crocodile smiled to himself. His plan was working. Soon he would have the monkey under his power.

"Very well," he said. "Hop onto my back."

So the monkey jumped onto the crocodile's back, and away they went up the river.

Suddenly the crocodile could keep his joke no longer. He laughed aloud.

"Now my wife will have the heart of a monkey and will soon be well!" he cried.

"Did you say the heart of a monkey, Mr. Crok Ka Dilly?" asked the monkey, his eyes growing very big and round.

"Yes," laughed the crocodile. "Our doctor said that my wife will be well if she eats the heart of a monkey."

The monkey looked around at the water. He was trapped. He scratched under his chin, but that didn't help. Then he scratched behind his ears. That helped.

"I should have thought of that myself," said the monkey at last. "The heart of a monkey is the very best thing in the world to take away a pain in the bones."

The crocodile was very much surprised to hear the monkey say this. "I can see you are a fine fellow," he remarked. "Are you really a doctor, Mr. Mon Key Dee?"

"Indeed I am!" replied the monkey. "If you crocodiles didn't always have so much water in your ears, you would have heard of the famous Dr. Mon Key Dee!"

"It is very kind of you to give your heart to my wife," the crocodile remarked.

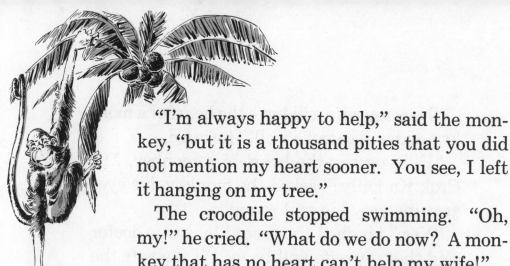

"I'm always happy to help," said the monkey, "but it is a thousand pities that you did not mention my heart sooner. You see, I left it hanging on my tree."

The crocodile stopped swimming. "Oh, my!" he cried. "What do we do now? A monkey that has no heart can't help my wife!"

"We must go back and get it. Don't you think so?" asked the monkey.

"Yes, that is best," agreed the crocodile.

So he turned around, and back down the river they went, together.

When the monkey was safe among the branches of his tree, he looked down at the crocodile. "Ha! Ha!" he laughed. "I had my heart with me all the time."

Then he began to chatter in such a loud voice that all the other monkeys in the jungle came to see what was happening.

Soon they were all screaming. One of them even hit the crocodile with a coconut.

That is how the war between the monkeys and the crocodiles started many years ago. From that day to this, no crocodile ever has been able to swim in the river without having monkeys scream at him.

THE MIGHTY CANDLE

Hodja was a wise and important man who lived in a village in old-time Turkey. Near the village was a mountain that most people believed was haunted by ghosts.

One day Hodja made a bet with two of his friends, Hassan and Mustafa. He was to spend a whole night alone, without any light, on the haunted mountain.

"If you stay there all night, alone and without a light, we'll give you a fine dinner," said Hassan. "We promise you."

"But if you fail," Mustafa said, "you will give us a dinner."

"I'll do it this very night," said Hodja. "The idea that ghosts haunt the mountain is nothing but foolishness."

At sundown the three men rode up the mountain. When they reached the top, Hassan and Mustafa got ready to leave Hodja. "We'll be back with your donkey in the morning," said Hassan. "Remember that we want no excuses if you can't keep your bet."

"I never make excuses," said Hodja. "Be off with you. Go home and count out the money for that dinner you are going to buy."

The two friends laughed and set off on the way back to the village. Hodja sat down and leaned against a tree.

Soon it was dark. A few candles twinkled faintly from the village below. They went out, one by one, as people went to bed. The night wind whistled coldly. Hodja was not afraid of ghosts, but he couldn't help wishing that he were home in his warm bed.

Midnight came and went. Shivering, Hodja lay down beside a tree and almost fell asleep. The only sound was the howling wind. The

only sight was one tiny spark of candlelight far below in the village. Sleepily, he wondered who was staying up so late, and why.

By morning, Hodja was very cold, but the rising sun soon warmed him. After a while his two friends came, leading his donkey.

"Thank goodness you are here!" cried Hodja. "I am very glad to see you."

"Did you see any ghosts?" asked Hassan.

"No," said Hodja. "Believe me, the cold is worse than any ghost." He ran to mount his donkey. "I've certainly earned a good dinner from the two of you."

"But, Hodja," said Mustafa, "you haven't won the dinner yet. Can you tell us, on your honor, that you had no light?"

"Light?" repeated Hodja.

"Yes, we understand that a candle burned in the village all night," said Hassan. "It was set in a window that faced the mountain. Didn't you see the light, Hodja?"

"Of course I saw it," replied Hodja, "but it was a mile away. It gave me no light."

He stopped speaking then, for he suddenly realized that his friends had played a trick on him. They had put the candle in the window, knowing he would see its light.

"It makes no difference whether the candle was a mile away or an inch," declared Mustafa. "The candle gave you light, and you were not supposed to have any."

"Remember—you never make excuses," said Hassan. "You have lost the bet, and now you will have to pay. We'll have dinner with you tonight, Hodja, if you please."

"A big dinner," Mustafa added. "We expect to be quite hungry."

"Very well," said Hodja, and the three men started down the mountain.

That evening Hodja greeted his two friends warmly. Then they were seated. After they had talked for several minutes, Hodja jumped to his feet. "Excuse me," he said. "I'll step into the kitchen to see about dinner."

In a minute he came back, shaking his head. "Not ready," he said and sat down.

Soon Hodja got up again. "I'll be right back," he said. Once more he returned, shaking his head. "Not ready yet. I'm sorry."

When he had done this a third time, his hungry friends began to wonder. "Hodja," said Hassan, "do you really have some food cooking out there in the kitchen?"

"The food I have is fit for a king," said Hodja. "Plenty of meat and rice, red ripe tomatoes, green peppers, and cabbage. It's all in a pot hanging directly over the flame."

Now the two friends felt much better. Their mouths watered, and they licked their lips. They kept looking at the door to the kitchen, but Hodja talked on. Every few minutes he went to the kitchen, but he always returned, shaking his head.

At last he said for the tenth time, "Not ready yet. I'm sorry."

"Hodja," Mustafa said, "could we see this dinner that you are cooking?"

"Yes, indeed, come and look at it," said Hodja, leading the way to the kitchen. A big pot full of meat, rice, and vegetables hung in the fireplace. Under it, instead of a fire, a candle was burning.

The surprised friends cried out, "Are you trying to cook with a candle?"

"Why not?" asked Hodja as though it was the usual thing to do. "If a candle in the village can light a mountain a mile away, it surely can cook food less than a foot away."

UNDER OUR FLAG

THE LEGEND OF BETSY ROSS

One summer morning in the year 1776, Mistress Betsy Ross sat sewing in the living room of her little house in Philadelphia. A bowl of roses stood on the drop-leaf table beside her, smelling sweetly of her garden. The ruffled curtains at the front window stirred in the warm summer breeze.

Suddenly Betsy heard footsteps outside. She put down her work and went to the window. Three men were coming up the path to her front door.

One of the men was George Ross, a member

of the Continental Congress. Another was Robert Morris, a well-known banker, and the third was General George Washington! Why were these three important men coming to see her, a young widow who took in sewing for a living?

Quickly, Betsy opened the door to her callers. "Good morning, gentlemen," she said as she made a deep, graceful curtsy.

George Ross, whom she knew, introduced her to the other gentlemen and explained why they had come to see her. "We have come to see you about the making of a flag," he said.

"The three of us have been asked by Congress to decide upon the right flag for our country," added Mr. Morris.

"Will you be seated?" Betsy asked politely. She felt happy to be chosen for this important work, but she also was a little frightened. She scarcely knew what to say or do.

"Our new nation still hasn't any flag of its own," General Washington explained. "Up to now, as you may know, different colonies and groups have used their own flags. For example, at the Battle of Bunker Hill, the soldiers carried several different kinds of flags."

"Benjamin Franklin likes the Rattlesnake Flag," put in Mr. Morris. "It has a picture of a coiled rattlesnake in the center, with the words, 'Don't Tread on Me,' below.

"The colony of Rhode Island has a white flag with the word 'Hope' on it and a picture of an anchor. It also has a field of blue with white stars in the background."

"I like stars," said General Washington. "The Washington family has a coat of arms in

the shape of a shield, with three five-pointed stars and three stripes on it. This coat of arms gave me an idea for a flag."

He took a piece of paper from his pocket on which he had drawn a picture of a flag. He showed the picture to Betsy and said, "Could you make a flag that looks like this?"

Betsy looked at the drawing. "These stars have six points, General Washington," she said. "Didn't you speak of five-pointed stars?"

"Yes," the general answered, "but how could stars with five points be cut?"

"Oh, that's easy," smiled Betsy. Quickly she picked up a piece of cloth, folded it neatly, and snipped it with her scissors. Then she unfolded the cloth and showed the general a five-pointed star.

"I learned to do this as a child," she said, "when I was helping my mother make patchwork quilts for our beds."

General Washington was pleased. "Will you make another five-pointed star?" he asked politely.

After Betsy had cut another star, the General said, "Mistress Ross, could you make this flag for us soon, and use five-pointed stars?"

"I've never made a flag before, but I'm sure I can," Betsy answered. "I'll have it finished by tomorrow. The flag will have thirteen red and white stripes with a blue field, as in your drawing. On the blue field I'll place a circle of white stars."

"You will do your country a great service if you make this flag," declared the General, taking her hand. "This will be a service that may never be forgotten."

After the gentlemen left, Betsy sat down for a moment to think. She felt honored to make the official flag of the Continental Army, but just how should she go about it? Before long, however, she had decided upon a plan that seemed good.

Taking her cape from a peg on the wall, she hurried down to the waterfront. She climbed aboard a ship anchored along the waterfront, and asked a seaman to show her the ship's flag. When he brought it to her, she looked at it long and carefully.

She noticed that the flag was bound with sailcloth to make it strong. She noticed that it had eyelets along one side, so that it could be fastened to a pole.

Next she went to see Mr. Morris in his office, and looked at another flag. She compared this flag with the ship's flag. In a short time she had figured out how she would cut and stitch the new Continental flag.

She hurried on to a store and bought the cloth for the flag. She bought white cloth, red cloth, and blue cloth. After that, she went home and began to sew. As she sewed, she thought about the flag she was making.

"There will be one stripe for each of the thirteen colonies," Betsy said to herself. "On the field of blue there will be a star for each of the colonies, too."

Betsy sewed until dark. "Delaware, Pennsylvania, New Jersey, Georgia, Connecticut, Massachusetts, Maryland, South Carolina, New Hampshire, Virginia, New York, North Carolina, and Rhode Island," she counted as she put the stars in place.

At last she folded her work and put it away.

Late the next day the flag was finished. It was taken directly to General Washington.

On June 14, 1777, the United States Congress voted that this flag be adopted as the national flag of our country. Since that time, June 14 has been known as Flag Day.

Our present flag greatly resembles the flag Betsy Ross made. However, many new stars have been added as new states have been admitted to the Union. There are now fifty stars, for there are fifty states.

The story of Betsy Ross and the first flag has been told over and over again. We can't be sure that all the things in the story actually happened. We do know, however, that Betsy Ross loved her country and made many flags.

If you were to visit Philadelphia today, you could see the small, brick house where Betsy Ross once lived and worked. This house still stands in the heart of the big city.

You might even imagine that you could see Betsy seated in her living room, wearing a long, full dress and ruffled cap. Her head would be bent over her sewing and her fingers would be flying, as she made the first flag for a new nation.

A PIONEER HOUSEWARMING

The Fishers—Father, Mother, Sally, Jimmy, and Grandmother Fisher—were one of the pioneer families who lived in Kentucky in 1798. All the people in the settlement were good friends. They worked hard, but they had fun, too, usually by helping one another.

It was a fine fall afternoon, and there were visitors at the Fisher home. Mrs. Scott and Mrs. Williamson had come to help plan the housewarming for Miss Lizzie and Mr. Watkins, who were to be married soon. The housewarming was to be held on Saturday evening.

"We'll be sure to have one good dessert, anyway," said Mrs. Williamson. "Harvey 'lined' a bee tree yesterday."

"How did he find the tree?" asked Jimmy.

"He placed a 'sweet bait' down on a stump at our spring where the bees come for water," explained Mrs. Williamson. "He knew that as soon as the bees had gathered their load of sweets, they would fly in a straight line to their tree home. He watched the way they went and followed them to the tree."

64

"You said that Harvey 'lined' a bee tree," said Sally. "Do you mean that he found the tree by following the bees as they flew in a straight line?"

"That's right," said Mrs. Williamson. "As soon as he found the tree, he cut several gashes in it. Then he ran home for help. His father went back with him, and they chopped down the tree. They brought home three gallons of honey, even though they left some honey for the bees to live on this winter."

"Why did Harvey cut gashes in the tree?" asked Jimmy.

"So that no one would take the honey while he was away," answered Mrs. Williamson. "A

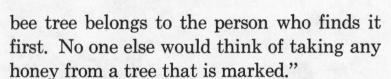

bee tree belongs to the person who finds it first. No one else would think of taking any honey from a tree that is marked."

"It is good you found some honey," said Mrs. Fisher. "Now we'll be sure to have something sweet for the supper. I haven't any maple sugar left to take. It didn't last very well this year—chiefly because each of my children has a sweet tooth, I guess."

"Harvey and Hannah are not fond of maple sugar, so I have some cakes of it left," said Mrs. Williamson. "When they were made, I wrapped them in extra bark, and the sugar has kept fresh all summer. I'll have Hannah melt some of it into sirup and make some popcorn balls for the supper."

"I'm glad you spoke about popcorn balls," said Mrs. Scott. "Jonathan has been helping Mr. Watkins pick his crop of corn this week. Jonathan suggested that the men and boys husk the corn the night we have the housewarming. What do you think of that?"

Mrs. Fisher and Mrs. Williamson thought it was a very good idea.

Grandma thought a husking bee would be fine, too, but she wanted to finish planning the supper. "Honey and popcorn balls do not make a feast," she said. "What kind of meat shall we have?"

"Jimmy has learned to 'bark a squirrel,'" said Sally. "Suppose we let him get some tender young squirrels for us."

The women agreed that this was a good idea, and they asked Jimmy to get some squirrels. This made him feel proud and important. He was really growing up!

Any pioneer boy was proud of being able to "bark a squirrel," for it was hard to do. One had to shoot off the bark of a tree so close to a squirrel that the force killed it. Then the squirrel's body would not be hurt by bullets, and no meat would be wasted.

The women planned the rest of the food. The table must be filled with the best that each family in the settlement could give. Besides squirrel, there would be venison, bear, and turkey. There would be cabbage, potatoes, corn, corn-meal dodgers, and ashcake.

Johnnycake served with honey and maple sirup would be dessert. There would be apples and popcorn balls, too.

"Now what about presents?" Grandma

asked. "Lizzie is a fine girl, and I want her to have the best we can give her."

"Mr. Williamson has made Miss Lizzie a fine broom," said his wife. "He's been working on it every night for a week."

This was true. Mr. Williamson had sat hour after hour, working to make a broom from a very young hickory tree.

He had split one end of the little tree into many fine splinters, about ten inches long. These splinters made the brush part. Around the top of the splinters, he had tied a willow twig. He had to use a twig, because he had no string or rope. The other end of the young tree formed the handle.

"I'm sure Miss Lizzie will need the turkey wings I have saved for her," said Grandma. "How in the world could anybody keep dust off things without turkey wings!"

"I believe we have thought of almost everything," said Mrs. Williamson. "Hannah and I saved the feathers from our geese all summer, and we have made some fine feather pillows for Miss Lizzie and Mr. Hiram."

"Don't forget my candles and the chair that Father made," said Mrs. Fisher.

"Nor our quilt," added Sally.

"Hurrah for the housewarming," said Mrs. Scott. "I believe we're ready for it."

Early Saturday evening the neighbors went to the home of the newly-married couple. The new house was a fine log cabin that the men of the settlement had helped Hiram Watkins build during the summer.

The girls and boys played games outside while the grown people gathered around the table for the feast. Wooden platters held the meats. Wooden bowls held the cabbage and other vegetables. Wooden plates held bread. Nuts, apples, and popcorn balls were piled high in the center of the table.

Because Grandma Fisher was the oldest person at the table, Mr. Watkins asked her to offer thanks before the meal began.

"We thank Thee, dear Lord," she prayed, "for these friends, for Thy kindness to us at all times, and for the blessings of life. Bless all of us and give us many more happy days together. Amen."

As soon as the grown people had eaten, the children came to the table. After they had finished eating, the women and girls washed the dishes while the men and boys went to the barn for the husking bee.

They made a game of their work. The corn was heaped in a great pile on the floor of the barn. The men and boys chose two leaders, or captains. Then each leader chose the people he wanted for his side. The fun was in seeing which side could husk the most corn in a given time.

The boys worked as hard as the men, and before long the great pile of corn had been husked. In its place were two piles of fine yellow ears. Hiram Watkins counted the ears in each pile and called out loudly, "Harvey Williamson's side won!"

Harvey's men lifted him up on their shoulders and carried him around. Everyone on both sides clapped and shouted.

When the husking bee was over, the women and girls joined the men and boys. Then the square dancing began, right there in the barn. A fiddler supplied the music and someone in the group called out directions, telling the dancers what to do.

Tonight both Roger Simpson and Hugh Jackson had brought along their fiddles.

"Come on, Hugh, play 'Old Zip Coon' for us," cried Grandma Fisher as she took her place on the floor with Mr. Fisher.

While a number of couples danced, the other people clapped and sang.

On into the night the older people sang and danced while the children watched or played games. For a few hours the pioneers were able to put aside all their worries.

After the party all of them would have to work hard again. They would have to clear the forest and plow fields and build homes in the wilderness. There was still danger of Indian attacks, but tonight there was nothing but gaiety in the settlement.

AN ARMY OF TWO

Abby Bates stood quietly watching her father ride away down the dusty road. When he was completely out of sight, she sighed and slowly shook her head.

Mr. Bates was a lighthouse keeper, but he was also a good neighbor. He had just left to help a neighbor care for a sick cow.

"I wish that Father hadn't gone away and left you and me alone at the lighthouse," said Abby. "I'm afraid, now that there is a war going on."

Abby had thought that she was talking to her older sister, Rebecca, but she turned around and found that Rebecca was nowhere in sight. She ran toward the small white cottage behind the lighthouse.

"Becky! Becky!" she called as she hurried through the cottage and out the front door.

"Where can Rebecca be?" thought Abby as she sat down on the front steps. "She knows as well as I do that we have dishes to wash and beds to make and the lamp in the lighthouse to polish and——"

As soon as she thought of the lighthouse,

Abby jumped up. She ran down the path and through the door of the tall white building. Taking two steps at a time, she climbed the narrow, winding stairway all the way to the top of the tower.

She found Rebecca standing on the narrow ledge outside the tower, looking through a spyglass. "Rebecca Bates, what are you doing up here with Father's spyglass?" she called.

Rebecca leaned farther over the railing that ran along the ledge. "I'm watching for British ships," she said calmly. "Looking for enemy ships while Father is away is far more important than doing housework."

"I know, but Father said the British warships are so far away that there is no cause for worry," said Abby. "He wants us to take care of the cottage and the lamp, just as Mother would if she were still alive."

Rebecca set the heavy spyglass down carefully and turned to face her sister.

"Now, Abby, don't get upset," she said. "Remember you are only nine years old, and you don't understand about war. Let's sit down here for a minute and talk. I'll try to explain a few things."

The girls sat down on the ledge and looked out over Scituate Bay. Here and there, fishing boats and tall schooners could be seen at anchor. Far to the left, back of a sandy ridge that circled the bay, was the little village of Scituate. Rebecca and Abby had been there often with their father.

"Abby," Rebecca began, "before you and I were born our country fought a great war with England for independence. Now we are fighting another war with England. This war began two years ago, in 1812, and no one knows yet who is winning.

"The British have many more ships than we have, and it's hard to tell where they will attack next. Father knows all this, but he didn't want to frighten you. Now do you see why I have to watch for enemy ships while he is away from the lighthouse?"

"Y-e-e-s," said Abby slowly, thinking over what Rebecca had just said. Then she looked out across the water and saw, far away, a strange ship coming toward the bay. "What kind of ship is that?" she cried.

Rebecca grabbed the spyglass and whirled around to get a good look at the ship. She

felt her hands shaking as she held the spyglass
up and peered out to see.

"It's a British warship!" she whispered.
"It's coming in fast, for the tide is high at this
time of day."

"Oh, no!" cried Abby, pulling on Becky's
arm. "Let's run away. Come on!"

"Wait a minute!" said Rebecca. "I want to
see what the ship is going to do. Oh, my! Now
the men are dropping anchor and lowering
rowboats into the water. Soldiers in red coats
are getting into the boats."

Rebecca put down the spyglass and began
to pace back and forth on the narrow ledge.

Abby squeezed herself up against the wall, trying to keep out of her sister's way.

"Abby, we have to think of some way to get rid of that ship," said Rebecca. "There's no time to run to the village and warn people. The British probably plan to burn the fishing boats and the village, too."

"What can we do?" asked Abby with her teeth chattering. "We haven't any guns, and if we had some, we wouldn't know how to shoot them."

Rebecca was thinking hard. Suddenly she cried, "Follow me, Abby."

She led the way down the winding stairway and up the path to the cottage. Then she went to her father's room and took his fife and drum off the shelf.

"Abby," she said quickly, "I'll play the fife, and you beat the drum. The only tune I know is 'Yankee Doodle,' but that will do. Now let's hurry out to the ridge."

Carrying the fife and drum, the girls ran behind the sandy ridge. From this spot they could no longer see the rowboats, but they knew that by now the rowboats must have entered the bay.

"I'll start to play the fife, and you start to beat the drum," said Becky in a low voice. "The soldiers in the rowboats won't see us, but they will hear us."

"Why do you want them to hear us?" asked Abby. "Why don't we keep quiet and hide?"

"We want to make them think that an army is marching down to fight them," said Becky. "Let's hope they never find out that we are an army of two!"

Rebecca began to play the fife, and Abby began to beat the drum. They walked back and forth behind the ridge and played "Yan-kee Doodle" over and over again.

After what seemed a long time, they heard

the sound of guns. Rebecca stopped playing the fife and listened. "I guess we've failed," she said. "The British seem to be firing at the village. We'd better go home."

The girls started toward the cottage, but Becky wanted to know what was happening in the village. "Stay here," she said to Abby. "I'm going to the top of the ridge."

When Becky reached the top, she shaded her eyes with her hands and looked out across the water. "Abby! Oh, Abby!" she cried. "We haven't failed! The rowboats have gone back, and the warship is heading out to sea. We've won! We've won!"

"Then where is the sound of guns coming from?" cried Abby. "Who is shooting?"

"The men in the village are firing at the warship," replied Rebecca. "When they heard us playing, I guess they thought that we were a big army coming to help them."

Rebecca came running back to her little sister. She felt relieved, proud, and happy, all at the same time.

"Well," she said, "let's go home now and wash the dishes and make the beds and polish the lamp. Father will be home soon."

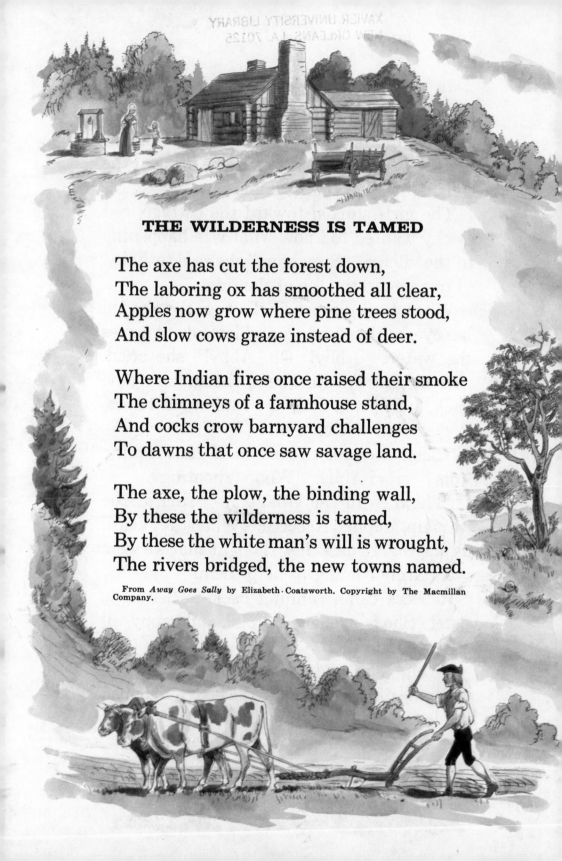

THE WILDERNESS IS TAMED

The axe has cut the forest down,
The laboring ox has smoothed all clear,
Apples now grow where pine trees stood,
And slow cows graze instead of deer.

Where Indian fires once raised their smoke
The chimneys of a farmhouse stand,
And cocks crow barnyard challenges
To dawns that once saw savage land.

The axe, the plow, the binding wall,
By these the wilderness is tamed,
By these the white man's will is wrought,
The rivers bridged, the new towns named.

From *Away Goes Sally* by Elizabeth Coatsworth. Copyright by The Macmillan Company.

LITTLE HOUSE ON THE PRAIRIE

Mr. and Mrs. Ingalls and Laura, Mary, and Carrie moved from the big Wisconsin woods to the prairie land of Kansas.

Pa picked a spot for the new house where he could get logs from trees that grew along a creek. He couldn't build the house alone, so Ma helped him. Then she hurt her ankle, and work on the house had to wait.

One afternoon Pa came merrily whistling up the creek road. Ma and the girls had not expected him home from hunting so soon. As soon as he saw them he shouted, "Good news!"

From *Little House on the Prairie* by Laura Ingalls Wilder. Copyright, 1935, Laura Ingalls Wilder. Reprinted by permission of Harper & Brothers.

They had a neighbor, only two miles away on the other side of the creek. Pa had met him in the woods. They were going to trade work, and things would be easier for everyone.

"He's a bachelor," said Pa. "He says that he can get along without a house better than you and the girls can. So he's going to help me first. Then, as soon as he gets his logs ready, I'll help him."

Now they need wait no longer for the house, and Ma need not do any more work on it.

"How do you like that, Caroline?" Pa asked Ma joyfully.

Ma said, "That's good, Charles. I'm glad."

Early next morning Mr. Edwards came. He was lean and tall and brown. He bowed to Ma and called her "Ma'am," politely, but he told Laura that he was a wildcat from Tennessee. He wore tall boots, a ragged jumper, and a coonskin cap.

He was a fast worker. In one day he and Pa built those log walls as high as Pa wanted them. They joked and sang while they worked, and their axes made the chips fly.

On top of the walls they set up a skeleton roof of slender poles. In the south wall they cut a tall hole for a door. In the west wall they cut square holes for windows.

Laura couldn't wait to see the inside of the house. As soon as the tall hole was cut, she ran inside. Everything was striped there. Long stripes of sunshine came through the cracks in the west wall, and stripes of shadow came down from the poles overhead. Through the cracks between the logs she could see stripes of the grassy prairie.

The sweet smell of the prairie mixed with the sweet smell of cut wood. Then, as Pa cut away the logs to make the window hole in the west wall, chunks of sunshine came in. When he had finished, a big block of sunshine lay on the ground inside the house.

Around the door opening and the window holes, Pa and Mr. Edwards nailed thin slabs against the cut ends of the logs. The house

was finished, all but the roof. The canvas wagontop must serve as the roof for now. The walls were solid and the house was large, much larger than the tent. It was a nice house.

Pa said he would build a fireplace as soon as he could. He would hew out slabs to make a solid roof, too, before winter came, and he would make a strong door. He would lay a floor and make beds and tables and chairs. However, all that work must wait until he had helped Mr. Edwards build a cabin.

Mr. Edwards said he would go home now, but Pa and Ma said he must stay to supper. Ma had cooked an especially good supper because they had company. There was stewed jack rabbit with white-flour dumplings and gravy. There was hot corn bread flavored with bacon fat. There was molasses to eat on the corn bread.

Mr. Edwards said he surely did enjoy that supper. Then Pa brought out his fiddle. Mr. Edwards stretched out on the ground to listen. First Pa played for Laura and Mary. He played their favorite song, and he sang it. Laura liked it best of all, because Pa's voice went down deep, deep, deeper:

" 'Oh, I am a Gypsy King!
I come and go as I please!
I pull my old nightcap down
And take the world at my ease.' "

Then his voice went deeper, deeper down, deeper than the very oldest bullfrog's, as he brought his song to an end:

" 'Oh, I am a Gypsy King!' "

"Oh, sing it again, Pa! Sing it again!" Laura cried, before she remembered that children must be seen and not heard.

Pa went on playing, and everybody began to dance. Mr. Edwards rose up on one elbow. Then he jumped up and danced.

He danced like a jumping jack there in the moonlight. Pa's fiddle kept on rollicking, and his foot kept tapping the ground. Laura's hands and Mary's hands were clapping together, and their feet were tapping, too.

Baby Carrie couldn't sleep in all that music. She sat up in Ma's lap, looking at Mr. Edwards with round eyes, and clapping her little hands and laughing. Even the firelight and the shadows danced.

Only the new house stood still and quiet in the darkness of the night. Then at last the big moon rose and shone brightly on the gray walls of the house.

Mr. Edwards said he must go. It was a long way back to his camp on the other side of the woods and the creek. He took his gun, and said good night to Laura and Mary and Ma. He said a bachelor got mighty lonesome, and he surely had enjoyed this evening.

"Play, Ingalls!" he said. "Play me down the road." So while he went down the creek road and out of sight, Pa played, and Pa and Mr. Edwards and Laura sang with all their might:

> " 'Old Dan Tucker was a fine old man;
> He washed his face in the frying-pan,
> He combed his hair with a wagon wheel,
> And died of a toothache in his heel.
>
> " 'Get out of the way for old Dan Tucker!
> He's too late to get his supper!
> Supper's over and the dishes washed,
> Nothing left but a piece of squash!
>
> " 'Old Dan Tucker went to town,
> Riding a mule, leading a houn' . . . !' "

Far over the prairie rang Pa's big voice and
Laura's little one. Faintly from the creek bot-
toms came a last whoop from Mr. Edwards:

" 'Get out of the way for old Dan Tucker!
He's too late to get his supper!' "

When Pa's fiddle stopped, they could not
hear Mr. Edwards any more. Only the wind
rustled in the prairie grasses. The big yellow
moon was sailing high overhead. The sky was
so full of light that not one star twinkled in it.
Then, from the deep woods by the creek, a
nightingale began to sing.

HARVEY AND HIGGINS DELIVERY

Jim Harvey and Dan Higgins lived in a small town in the Middle West. It was a nice town on the edge of a lake, with pleasant houses and tree-bordered streets. Jim and Dan lived next door to each other. They were nine and ten years old and great friends.

The birthdays of Jim and Dan came on the same day. This was the thirtieth of July, right in the middle of the summer vacation.

On the day that Jim was nine and Dan ten, Jim woke up early. There were no presents by his bed. At the breakfast table there were no presents. No one seemed even to know that it was his birthday. After breakfast he went out in the yard and leaned over the fence to talk to his friend Dan.

"Hello, Dan!" said Jim.

"Hello, Jim!" said Dan.

"I didn't get any presents for my birthday."

"I didn't either."

"Do you suppose they forgot?"

Just then both boys were called.

"Jim," said Mr. Harvey, "come down to the barn. I have something to show you."

From *America Travels* by Alice Dalgliesh. Copyright, 1933, by The Macmillan Company.

The barn was dark when Jim went into it, and he could not see very clearly. In one stall he found Bess, the horse that his father used to pull the buggy. In the other stall he found something else—something that looked like a pony. It was small and dark brown.

"What do you think of that for a birthday present?" asked his father.

"A birthday present! Dad! Is that brown pony really all mine?"

His father nodded. "Take the halter and lead him out to show Danny."

Jim took the halter and led the little pony out, very carefully. His heart was thumping so that he could hardly breathe. Now he and the small brown pony were in the sunny yard.

"Hi, Danny!" Jim's shout died off suddenly. There was Dan with a pony almost like his own. Both fathers were watching the boys and laughing.

"You'll find saddles in the barn," said Mr. Harvey. "I guess you both know what to do with the saddles, don't you?"

They did. For a year the boys had wanted a pony more than anything else in the world. They had learned to ride Tom Smith's pony. They had hoped only for one pony. Now there were two.

"This is the best day we have had in all our lives," Jim said to Dan. They rode the ponies and gave turns to all the children who lived in their neighborhood.

For several weeks everything went well. Then Mr. Harvey and Mr. Higgins, who were business partners, lost a great deal of money.

"I'm afraid the ponies will have to go," said Mr. Harvey. "They cost a good deal to keep."

"Oh, Dad, can't we keep them? Can't we keep them if we earn money to feed them?"

"How can you earn money?"

"We'll think of a way."

Jim and Dan thought and thought, but they could not think of a plan. At last an idea came to Danny. "Jim, I know! Let's fix up our wagon and deliver things for the stores."

"Would they let us?"

"They'll have to. Come on!"

The boys decided to fix up the wagon to make it look better. They decided to paint it bright blue. On each side they painted in rather crooked letters:

HARVEY AND HIGGINS
DELIVERY

Thus Harvey and Higgins started in business. It was surprising how the business grew. At first they delivered a few packages for the hardware store. Then they took flowers for the florist.

Soon the smaller stores began to find out that people liked to have the blue wagon and the two small ponies trot up to their door and deliver a package. So each day after school there were interesting packages to be taken around town.

One afternoon Harvey and Higgins left the baker's with a most exciting package. There were other packages, too, but placed carefully in the middle of the wagon was a large box done up in white paper and tied with an enormous silver bow.

Inside was Dorothea May Armstrong's birthday cake. Dorothea May lived in the largest house in town, a house to which Harvey and Higgins had always wanted to deliver a package.

"Do you suppose they'll ask us to take it in?" asked Jim as they drove carefully along Main Street. "I've always wanted to see what the inside of that house is like."

"Maybe they will ask us in," said Danny. "Look, Jim. What's the crowd on the corner over there by the hotel?"

"Let's drive over and see," said Jim.

By the hotel a crowd had gathered and was staring curiously at a large black object.

"It's one of those new horseless carriages!" said Dan excitedly. "I never saw one of them before. Let's go nearer."

They drove nearer. The strange black carriage was making queer, purring sounds. It coughed and choked. The crowd laughed.

The tall man who sat in the carriage looked annoyed. He climbed out and turned a handle

in front of the machine, ran back, climbed in, and turned something else. Then the machine leaped forward with a mighty roar.

The ponies of Harvey and Higgins never had seen anything like that noisy object! Like twin streaks of lightning off they went, with Harvey shouting "Whoa!" and Higgins hanging onto the lines.

Packages were scattered everywhere. When finally the ponies came to a standstill, Dan and Jim looked blankly at each other.

"The birthday cake!"

Sadly they went back along Main Street, walking beside the ponies. Friends handed them the packages. Some were much the worse for wear. Close by the hotel a boy who was in Dan's class at school held the large package tied with silver ribbon.

"Hey, Danny! This slid off just as you were starting. I caught it!"

Dan and Jim heaved sighs of relief. "Maybe it isn't hurt." They untied the box carefully and peered into the package. A dozen or so boys and girls gathered around and peered, too.

There was the cake quite unharmed, glittering with its white frosting and pink flowers and silver trimmings. It was safe!

Then Dan happened to look up at the clock. Three forty-five, and the party was to be at four! The Armstrong house was at the other end of town. They couldn't make it. For the first time Harvey and Higgins would fail to deliver a package. They would be disgraced.

"Well, boys! I'm sorry my automobile scared your ponies," said a voice. "I'll make it good with you about those packages."

They looked up to see the owner of the car that had made the trouble. The man looked so friendly that in a minute they were telling him the whole sad tale of the birthday cake.

"Can't deliver it, you say? Why not? There's my machine right around the corner. It will go there in two shakes of a lamb's tail. Get a boy to drive your ponies home and off we'll go. You'll be the first boys in this town to ride in an automobile!"

The first boys in the town to ride in an automobile! Harvey and Higgins could scarcely believe it was not a dream.

There they were, rattling along Main Street. Danny was holding the box with the cake very carefully on his knees. People stood still on the sidewalks to look at them.

Jim hoped that none of the boys in his class at school would miss the sight. Dan wondered if riding a horseless carriage were dangerous, but he didn't much care.

There was a bang and a clatter. The machine stopped short, and no amount of coaxing would make it go. The gentleman got out, lifted the hood in front, and peered inside. Then he came back, got a tool, and fussed with the machinery. It seemed a long time before the automobile was ready to start.

"I think we could have got there quicker with our ponies!" whispered Jim to Dan.

A crowd of small boys gathered to watch what was going on. They began to laugh.

"Get a horse!" cried one of the boys. Then they all chanted loudly in chorus:

"Get a horse, Mister! Get a horse!"

Suddenly, when the car was cranked, something inside it began to purr softly. With a cough and a snort they were off again!

In no time at all now they were puffing and snorting up the driveway of the Armstrong home. The butler came out of the house. His eyes were almost popping out of his head. Then Dorothea May came running out, too.

"Oh, Daddy! Mother! Bob! Susan!" she called out. "Here's one of those queer new horseless carriages!"

The Armstrong family came out and stood on the doorstep. Danny climbed out of the car and handed the box to Dorothea May.

"Your birthday cake!" he said. "A little late, I'm afraid, but it might never have got to your house at all."

Then he climbed into the car again, and it puffed and snorted down the drive.

"I'm glad the ponies ran away!" whispered Jim to Dan. "If they hadn't run away, we wouldn't have been the first boys in this town to ride in a horseless carriage."

REACHING UP

THE BEADED MOCCASIN

Smallboy was an Indian boy who lived in the North Woods of Canada. He lived in a cabin with his grandmother, his big brother, Masha, his big sister, White Cloud, and his very little brother, Noisy Wren.

For some time Smallboy had wanted a dog of his own, but he had no money to buy one. Then one day he found his dog. It was an injured, half-wild dog that the Indians called a bad-medicine dog, but Smallboy didn't care.

He nursed the dog back to health and named him Windy. They became good friends. Windy was soon so tame that Smallboy began to teach him all the things an Indian sled dog needs to know to be of use in the wilderness.

Today Smallboy stood in the big woods. He was teaching Windy a new word. "Whis!" he said over and over. Windy watched him with uplifted paw. "Whis" means "Go away."

Smallboy was not scolding his dog. He was teaching him the trick that every Indian in the North Woods must teach his dog.

The trick was for the dog to go down the trail alone and return to his master. If a cap or some other piece of clothing were tied to his collar, anyone he met would know that the dog's master was in trouble. He would follow the dog back over the trail.

Windy had nothing at all tied to his collar. Smallboy was just trying to get him used to the word and make him understand that he was to go to the cabin and return. Over and over they practiced.

When evening came, Windy and Smallboy went down the trail to the cabin together. White Cloud opened the door, her eyes filled with curiosity. "Why do you teach your dog such a foolish trick?" she asked. "Foolish word, too—whis, whis."

101

At first Smallboy paid no attention, but White Cloud continued to mutter to herself the words, "Whis, whis."

Smallboy decided to explain. "Good Indian teach dog that trick," he said. "Good squaw know, too, that if dog come to cabin with something tied on collar, that means brave in trouble in woods."

"Brave!" said White Cloud and tossed her head. "You only boy!"

"No! Brave!" Smallboy thumped his chest. Then they both began to laugh, and nothing more was said about the word that night.

On the afternoon of the next day, Smallboy's grandmother placed a shining tin pail in his hands. "The great painter has swept his brush over the trees, making the leaves red and gold," she said. "He has touched the berries on the high bushes, painting them rosy red. Soon winter will be on the way."

Smallboy knew that his grandmother really meant that the high-bush cranberries were ripe, and she wanted them for jam. So he put on his red cap and warm jacket and started out of the cabin with the pail.

"Wah, wah wah," screamed Noisy Wren, stamping his tiny moccasins on the floor.

"The papoose do war dance. I take him with me," said Smallboy. The boys went out the door together, and Windy joined them.

Down the narrow path between the tall pines and the snow-white birches went the two boys and the white dog. Deeper and deeper into the woods they went, with Smallboy filling the shining pail with berries. Noisy Wren ran ahead, kicking up pine needles and chattering at the gray-and-white snowbirds.

At last the pail was full. Smallboy sat down on a fallen tree to rest. Windy stretched out at his feet. Suddenly the boy lifted his head. The woods were strangely silent. Only

103

the twittering of birds and the soft lapping of the distant water could be heard. What had become of the laughing voice and the patter of Noisy Wren's feet?

Smallboy leaped to his feet and held his breath to listen. The trail was silent. The little one, the little one was gone!

"Noisy Wren! Noisy Wren!" he cried, making a cup of his hands. The only sound that came back to him was the hollow echo of his own voice.

It began to grow dark and Smallboy stumbled over the rough trail. He dared not take his eyes off the ground. Then he saw a small white object beside a fallen tree. It was a little white moccasin.

Smallboy's heart sank. He knew that it was one of a pair White Cloud had made for their baby brother. He picked it up and turned it over and over in his hands. Noisy Wren was such a little boy.

He brushed tears from his eyes and tried to swallow the lump in his throat. Night was near, but he dared not go for help. He could not leave the papoose alone in the woods.

Then a cold wet nose pressed against his

hand, and Smallboy looked down into a pair
of understanding brown eyes. Windy!

Why had he not thought of sending Windy
for help before? Surely White Cloud would
remember Windy's trick, the trick he had
explained to her. She would know he was in
trouble if he sent his dog to the cabin with
something tied to his collar.

Smallboy looked at the white moccasin
with the blue beads. It was the very thing
to send. With trembling fingers, he tied it
to the dog's collar.

"Go for help, Windy!" he cried. "Whis!
Whis!" Then he pointed down the trail.

Quickly, Windy turned and trotted off down the trail. The white moccasin bobbed at his collar as he disappeared.

Smallboy could do nothing but wait and hope that Windy would remember the trick he had practiced so often. Would Windy scratch at the cabin door to be let in? Would White Cloud remember and send help?

Time dragged by. After what seemed hours, Smallboy saw a faint light far down the trail. Then he heard a voice calling him. It was his brother, Masha, coming with a lantern. Windy was running at his heels. White Cloud had remembered Windy's trick!

The two boys and the dog plunged into the dark overgrown wilderness to find the lost papoose. Soon Windy stopped and lifted a paw. His sharp ears had caught a sound.

Smallboy heard it, too. It was the sound Noisy Wren made when he was angry or waking up from a nap. Masha looked at Smallboy and smiled knowingly. "The small one has been asleep in the big woods," he said.

"Wah, wah, wah," cried the papoose. Masha turned the lantern toward the sound, and the boys saw their little brother doing a

war dance under a birch tree. As he stamped his small feet on the ground, they could see that he wore only one beaded moccasin.

"You take lantern," said Masha to Smallboy. "I carry big chief." He set the papoose on his broad shoulders. Smallboy followed with the lantern and the pail of cranberries. Running ahead, Windy led them home.

When they were safely inside the cabin, White Cloud looked at Smallboy proudly. "You a brave, not a boy," she said. "You teach Windy good trick and good word, too."

Smallboy was proud and happy, but a brave must not show his feelings. So he laughed and gave White Cloud's hair a tweak. "Whis," he said, dancing around her. "Whis!"

OLD BRASS AND IRON

When Mr. Shaler decided to fix up the old mill, he asked the boys to clean up the rubbish dump. They were to have all the money they made by selling the old metal. The boys were delighted, because they had a special reason for wanting to make money.

Late the next afternoon there was not a can left to show where the rubbish dump had been. All the worthless junk had been hauled away, and the truck driver had promised to come back for the brass and iron, which the boys figured they could sell to the junk man.

Soon the truck returned and rattled to a stop. The driver, Pete Pennypacker, who was Eddie's older cousin, jumped out.

"Hop to it, boys," he said. "We're having an early dinner tonight. If two of you get up in the truck and pack the stuff tight, we can take it all in one load."

Everyone hustled, and soon the truck was filled and ready to go. Pete looked at the boys. "Marvin and Eddie," he said, "you sit on top of the load to see that nothing falls off. Heywood and Emery can sit with me."

Heywood and Emery climbed in beside Pete, and Marvin and Eddie crawled up on the load. Then they were off.

It didn't take the truck long to get into town. It bumped loudly over the canal bridge and slowed down as it went up the hill past Mrs. Binney's antique shop.

Mrs. Binney, who was standing outside with a man and a woman, glanced at the passing truck. Suddenly she waved her arms wildly, clutched her skirt, and began to run toward the truck. As she ran, her hair came undone and strung out behind her.

"I think she's calling," said Eddie. "I'll bet she wants us to stop."

"We didn't drop anything," said Marvin. Nevertheless, he extended a small iron pipe through the rear window, which had no glass,

and tapped Heywood on the shoulder. "Hey, tell Pete to stop," he yelled.

The truck pulled to the curb. Pete looked back and asked, "What did we lose?"

"Mrs. Binney——" Eddie began, but by that time Mrs. Binney had arrived.

Marvin leaned over the side of the truck. "Do you want something?" he asked politely.

"My—yes. Wait—till I catch—my breath." She stood for a minute, pushing up her hair and breathing very hard.

"I have some customers," she finally said, "who are looking for a brass bucket, and you have one on your truck." She pointed to it, "It's dented and has a crooked handle, but

will you sell it? It's just possible that my customers will like it."

Marvin looked at the sky. "That bucket's nearly as good as new," he said. "We'll sell it for ten dollars."

"Ten—!" gasped Mrs. Binney. She saw her customers coming. "All right," she said.

Marvin handed her the bucket. By now, the man and woman had reached the truck. "It's a fine bucket," Mrs. Binney told them, "heavy brass and extremely old. You can have it for fifteen dollars."

"We'll take it," said the lady. She handed Mrs. Binney the money, and Mrs. Binney gave Marvin a ten-dollar bill.

"Can we go now?" asked Pete. "We're having an early dinner, and I want to get home."

"Just a minute!" said the man who was with the woman. "Hold up! There's something else on your truck I want to see."

He pointed to something. "Isn't that an andiron sticking out?" he asked.

Marvin and Eddie tugged and twisted until they pulled out the andiron.

"Early colonial," the man whispered. Aloud he said, "Does it have a mate?"

111

The two boys began to search. Things clanked to the pavement. Then Eddie came up with a matching andiron and handed it to the man.

"They're rusty," said the man. "How much do you want for them?"

Behind the man, Mrs. Binney held up both hands and spread her fingers twice.

"Twenty dollars," said Eddie.

The man set the andirons on the sidewalk and gave Eddie the money.

"Can we go now?" asked Pete.

"Wait a minute," said Marvin.

The man was pulling something through the sideboards of the truck. Mrs. Binney held up seven fingers.

112

"Seven dollars," said Eddie.

"Keep a list," the man said to the woman. Then he began yanking at something else.

Mr. Delancey, who owned a gift shop, came up then and started poking at things. "How much for this?" he asked, holding up a little twisted piece of metal.

Marvin didn't even know what it was. He looked for Mrs. Binney, but she had her nose between the sideboards and didn't see him.

"Twenty dollars," Marvin said.

"It's a bargain," said Mr. Delancey. "I'll make a pile of things and pay the total."

Now people were beginning to come into town for dinner and the evening movie. Many of them came to the truck and began to make more piles of things on the sidewalk.

Heywood and Emery went to help Marvin and Eddie make up prices and take the money. Pete walked home to dinner.

Mrs. Binney backed away from the truck with a pair of bent candlesticks. "My! My!" she exclaimed. "This is a gold mine of brass and iron. Where did you find it?"

"Shaler's Mill dump," answered Marvin. Then he turned to Eddie. "Maybe we should

113

tell Mr. Shaler," he said. "He probably didn't know this stuff was worth so much money."

"He said we could sell anything we found," Eddie reminded him.

"I know. Just the same I'm going to go and telephone him. Keep an eye on things——"

Just then Mr. Shaler came on the run through the crowd. At first he looked as if he thought there had been an accident. When he found out exactly what was happening, he began to laugh.

"I was just going to telephone you," said Marvin. "We thought maybe you'd want some of the money——"

"Thank you," said Mr. Shaler, "but you've worked hard enough, long enough, and fast enough to have earned whatever you make."

Mr. Shaler left, and the sale went on. The boys continued to dig things from the truck, though most of the antiques were gone.

At last the crowd began to leave, and after a while the boys were alone with the truck. By the time they had tidied up the sidewalk, Pete had come back.

"There's no use going to the junk yard to-night," he said. "How much did you make?"

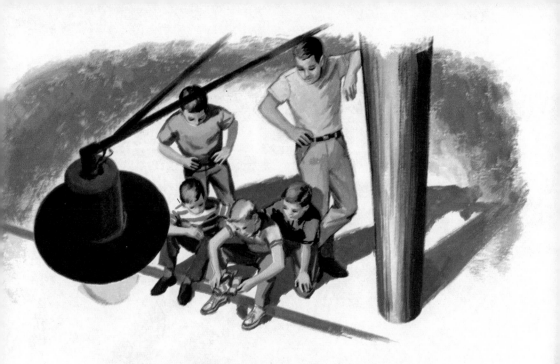

The boys sat down on the curb and counted their money. Altogether they had nearly two hundred and twenty dollars.

"Boy-oh-boy!" exclaimed Eddie.

"First thing tomorrow," shouted Heywood, "we'll go to Old Cappy and tell him we can buy the boat. Won't he be surprised?"

"Yep!" Marvin grinned. "We'll just peel off money as if it were cabbage leaves and tell him to untie the rope, please."

Pete took the boys home in his truck. They couldn't remember when they had been so tired and hungry, but they didn't care. They were too busy dreaming about the adventures they would have in their new boat.

A LITTLE SONG OF LIFE

Glad that I live am I;
That the sky is blue;
Glad for the country lanes,
And the fall dew.

After the sun the rain;
After the rain the sun;
This is the way of life,
Till the work be done.

All that we need to do,
Be we low or high,
Is to see that we grow
Nearer the sky.

From *Songs of a Wayside Lute* by Lizette Woodworth
Reese. Reprinted by permission of Rinehart & Company, Inc.

THE RAJAH'S SECRET

Jack Logan was sitting in front of his bedroom mirror. On his right knee he held a dummy that looked like a cowboy. Jack was a ventriloquist, and he was practicing with his dummy, Shorty. He was getting ready to appear on a television talent contest.

Jack pulled the string inside Shorty's hollow back, and the dummy's jaw moved. "You need a new dummy," Shorty squawked. "I'm worn out. My face is chipped, and my jaws clack when they come together."

Jack watched his own mouth in the mirror while he made the dummy say these words. His lips hardly moved. In his own voice, he said, "I need a new dummy, all right, but a good one would cost too much money."

At dinner that night Jack told his mother, "I just can't go on television with that old dummy. He's about to fall apart."

"I wish you could have a new one, but we can't afford it now," she replied. "Maybe for your birthday——"

"That's two months away!" cried Jack, but he knew there was no use arguing.

His mother looked thoughtful. "Maybe
Miss Clay can help you," she said.

Miss Clay was the lady who lived in the
big house up the street. Her Uncle Jasper
had been a famous ventriloquist. He had per-
formed all over the world and had become
rich before he died. The strange thing was
that he had left Miss Clay very little money.

"She may have some of her uncle's dummies," Mrs. Logan went on. "If she has, maybe she will lend you one for the contest."

"Oh, I didn't think of that!" Jack cried. Then he paused. "That's funny. Miss Clay has shown me many things that belonged to her uncle, but never any of his dummies. I'll bet he had some fancy ones, too. I'll go ask her tomorrow."

When Jack rang the bell at the big house, Miss Clay opened the door. "Hello, Jack," she said. "Won't you come in?"

Jack followed her into the gloomy house. It was filled with strange things that had belonged to her Uncle Jasper.

Uncle Jasper had been an unusual man. He never had spoken to his neighbors. He had lived all alone in this big house, interested only in collecting odd objects from foreign countries and working on magic tricks.

Jack told Miss Clay what he wanted and she replied, "Oh, dear, I'm afraid I can't help you. Uncle Jasper sent all his dummies to a museum—all, that is, except the Rajah."

"The Rajah?" asked Jack.

"Yes, Uncle Jasper said the Rajah was the finest dummy in the world—a gift from an Indian prince." She jumped up. "I'll show him to you if you'd like to see him."

Jack could hardly wait for her to return. When she came back, his eyes opened wide! She was carrying a little man dressed in a silk jacket, baggy pants, and a huge silk turban. He had black shaggy eyebrows and a long black beard.

"He looks real!" Jack gasped. The Rajah had flashing black eyes staring out over a fierce nose like a hawk's beak, but he didn't look mean. His mouth curved upward.

"May I try him?" asked Jack, and Miss Clay handed him the Rajah. Jack slipped his hand inside the dummy's hollow back and found the strings. He made the Rajah's mouth open and close. Then he made the Rajah say, "Hi, Miss Clay."

In his own voice he asked timidly, "May I use the Rajah for the talent contest?"

Miss Clay's face clouded over. "I must tell you something, Jack. Uncle Jasper always said it would be bad luck to let the Rajah leave the house. I don't believe in luck, of course, but there's something very strange about the Rajah.

"You see, Uncle Jasper had all his wealth in jewels. He always said that he was going to leave the jewels to me, but after he died, I couldn't find them.

"I found a note addressed to me which said, 'When the Rajah sleeps, he brings good fortune to his owner.' Somehow, I think the Rajah is connected with the missing jewels."

"Did you search the Rajah?" asked Jack.

"Oh, yes, every bit of him," said Miss Clay. "What puzzles me is that the note said, 'When the Rajah sleeps,' but he can't sleep. Even when you pull those strings, he shuts only one eye. The other eye won't move."

Jack wiggled a finger lightly on the left eye. It didn't move. "That eye won't close," he agreed, "so the Rajah can't sleep."

Miss Clay nodded. "Now you see why I can't let the Rajah out of the house."

Jack understood, but he was disappointed. He went home and practiced some more with the worn-out dummy, Shorty.

Suddenly the dummy's jaw stuck tight. Jack yanked hard on the string. Something gave. Stunned, he took his hand out of the dummy's back. At the other end of the string was a nail and a part of the wood from Shorty's jaw. The dummy was useless.

Nearly in tears, Jack ran to his mother. "We'll have Shorty fixed," she said, "but it may take a while. Maybe Miss Clay will let you practice with the Rajah if you stay at her house to do it."

Jack ran over to Miss Clay's house again. "Of course," she said, "work here in the living room. I'll be busy in the kitchen, but if you find out how to make the Rajah sleep, let me know."

After she left, Jack looked at the Rajah. "Why don't you sleep?" he asked.

He pulled a string and the Rajah's right eye closed. Holding this eye shut, Jack put his finger over the open left eye. When he had touched the left eye before, without holding the right one shut, the left eye had been firm. Now it seemed loose.

Jack pressed hard on the left eye. It began to roll shut. At the same time there was a whirring sound and a small click. The top of the Rajah's head jerked, and a gap showed between his forehead and his turbaned skull.

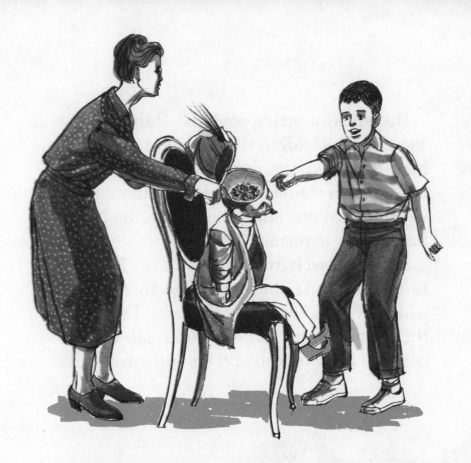

"Miss Clay!" Jack shouted. "Miss Clay!"

As she came hurrying in, Jack pointed at the opening in the Rajah's head. "Look!"

Miss Clay's hand shook as she reached for the turban and lifted it. It swung backward. Jack gasped. Flashes of red, blue, green, and every other color of a rainbow dazzled his eyes. Jewels sparkled in the light!

"The jewels! Uncle Jasper's wealth!" cried Miss Clay. She was half crying and half laughing. "You've found them, Jack."

124

She ran from the room and returned with a large velvet-lined box. Jack helped her put the jewels into the box. Then he pressed down on the turban. The skull moved back into place, and the line between the two parts completely disappeared. No wonder no one had discovered it before.

"How can I ever thank you, Jack?"

Jack thought for a minute before he said, "May I borrow the Rajah for the contest?"

"Borrow it! Why, the Rajah is yours—for always, Jack," answered Miss Clay.

Jack could hardly believe his ears. "Oh, thanks a million!" he said at last.

He took the Rajah in his arms and rushed home. He was sure he'd win the talent contest now. His mother was at the door when he arrived. The Rajah winked at her and said, "Hi, Mom. I'm in the family now."

"I don't understand——"

Jack explained how he had found the jewels. Then he turned to the dummy. "Isn't that right?" he asked. The Rajah nodded his head. "Yessiree," he said, "and I'm mighty glad to be rid of those jewels. They were giving me a terrible headache."

LISA'S SONG

When Lisa's mother asked her what she wanted for her birthday, she said, "One of Mrs. Puff's canaries, Mama." Then she added, "If it wouldn't cost to much."

Lisa lived in a part of California where all the families had one-acre ranches and raised things to make a living. Her parents raised hens and marketed the eggs. She knew that they could buy a fine laying hen for the same price as a canary.

Lisa's mother smiled. "It wouldn't cost too much," she said. "You are a big help to your papa and me, and you should have a nice present. Stop at Mrs. Puff's when you come from school and pick out a canary."

As soon as school was out, Lisa ran across the fields to the Puff ranch. Mrs. Puff met her at the door and led her to the sun porch where the cages hung.

"Your mama phoned you were coming," said Mrs. Puff, going toward a large cage filled with pretty yellow songbirds.

Lisa's eager eyes searched among them. "Where's Heinie?" she asked.

"Heinie? Oh, I've put him in a cage by himself in my room," said Mrs. Puff.

Lisa laughed. "You knew he was the one I wanted, didn't you?" she asked.

Mrs. Puff's face looked troubled. "I declare I didn't, dearie. Most people like the yellow canaries best. Wouldn't you like one of these in this cage?"

Lisa was silent. She didn't like to seem ungrateful, but it was Heinie, and no other, that she wanted for her own.

Birds are like people. Each one was different, and Heinie was *very* different. She loved the dark green of his coat and the perky black cap on one side of his head. Even more, she loved his voice. It was not high, like the voices of the yellow canaries, but low and sweet, like something dreamed.

Whenever she came to see him and spoke to him softly, he would open his bill and sing the sweetest melody she had ever heard.

"Lisa," said Mrs. Puff gently, "I'm sorry, but you have picked my best canary. I want to sell him to a Canary Training School. He may bring as much as fifty dollars."

Fifty dollars! Lisa turned away sadly. "I guess I don't want a canary, after all," she said politely. "Thank you just the same."

Mrs. Puff followed Lisa to the door, trying to think of something that would cheer her up. "Would you like to go along when I take Heinie to the training school?" she asked. "I'm going next Saturday."

Lisa nodded sadly as she left.

They started out early Saturday morning, and in an hour they were at the school. A large sign hung in the front window:

UPHAUS TRAINING SCHOOL FOR
CANARIES

While they waited to see the owner, Mrs. Puff showed Lisa about. One room had cages filled with yellow canaries.

"Will Heinie be put here?" Lisa asked.

"Oh, no, he'll be in that room with the glass door," said Mrs. Puff, pointing. "It's for gifted birds, and Heinie will have his own sound-proof cage."

Lisa stood on tiptoe and peered through the glass at the rows of closed, silent cages. "Why are canaries like Heinie kept in sound-proof cages?" she asked.

"They are being trained to sing a special song," Mrs. Puff explained. "For three months they're kept in cages where they hear nothing but a phonograph record playing the special song they are to learn.

"Young canaries imitate whatever sounds they hear. Canaries like Heinie will learn to whistle a human song. The canaries in there now are learning 'Yankee Doodle.'"

Lisa felt worse than ever now. She understood that Heinie had a great career ahead of him, but it seemed a sad life for a bird. She had planned to put his cage among the plants in her mother's sun room and let him sing what and when he pleased.

Just then Mrs. Uphaus called Mrs. Puff and Lisa into her office. "I brought a bird I'd like you to test as a possible pupil for your special training," said Mrs. Puff. Then she uncovered Heinie's cage.

Heinie sat inside looking so forlorn that Lisa bent over and spoke to him in low, soft tones. The green canary lifted his head and began to sing the melody that Lisa always had thought he sang only for her.

"Wonderful!" exclaimed Mrs. Uphaus. "Leave the bird here for a week on trial, Mrs. Puff. When you come back, I'll be ready to make you an offer. That's definite."

Lisa was silent on the ride home. She kept thinking of Heinie in that soundproof cage, being forced to learn a human song.

Mrs. Puff talked cheerfully, trying to make Lisa feel better. "Just think, dearie, many famous people buy canaries from Mrs. Uphaus. Wouldn't it be wonderful if Heinie should go to the White House?"

Even the idea that Heinie might sing for the President failed to cheer Lisa.

Her birthday was the following Saturday, and she worked in the garden most of the lovely spring day. It was her task to keep the weeds out of her mother's flower beds.

Later, when she was gathering eggs, she heard a car in the driveway.

"Lisa!" called her mother from the house. Lisa went slowly, not feeling in any mood to be pleasant to visitors.

Mrs. Puff sat in the living room with a small covered cage on her knees. Lisa's father and mother were there, too. "I have your birthday present for you, dearie," said Mrs. Puff with a beaming smile.

Lisa turned her face away. Why did her parents insist on giving her another canary when they knew she wanted only Heinie?

Mrs. Puff kept on talking as she took the cover off the stage. "All week at the training school he refused to sing a note. So Mrs. Uphaus didn't want him. Of course, I brought him right over to you."

Lisa quickly dropped to the cage. "Heinie, oh Heinie—it's you," she cried.

Heinie smoothed his ruffled feathers, opened wide his bill and sang his lovely—oh, so lovely—melody.

"That's it," Mrs. Puff whispered to Lisa's parents in something like awe. "He sings it only for her. It's Lisa's song!"

132

THE NEWCOMER

George and Tim were watching the moving van unload at the house next to George's. The house had been empty for a long time, but now some people were moving into it.

Suddenly Tim cried, "Look at that basket, George. It's full of dolls."

"It's just my luck," George said in disgust, "to have a whole houseful of girls move in next door. Since you moved to the other end of town, there isn't a fellow on the street to play with me. Every family has girls, and now some more are moving in."

Just then George's mother called him into the house. She had a tray of cookies and lemonade for him to take out on the porch. "George," she said, handing him the tray, "I thought later you boys might take a plate of cookies to our new neighbors next door."

George's face clouded. "Oh, Mom! I don't want to go over there, honest I don't. They have a whole houseful of girls."

"I don't think so, George," said his mother. "I understand they have only one child."

"Anyway, it's a girl, and she must be an awful sissy. Tim and I saw the men carry in a big basketful of dolls!"

"The child's name is Francis, but I thought it was a boy. That *can* be a girl's name, too, so maybe I'm mistaken."

"Sure you are!" broke in George. "No boy would play with all those dolls."

"Well, the newcomer is in a wheel chair, I do know that," said George's mother. "I know, too, that it's hard for any child, boy or girl, to move to a strange town."

134

George didn't answer, and he slammed the screen door behind him as he went back to join Tim on the porch.

The boys ate their cookies and drank their lemonade in silence after George had told Tim what his mother had said. The cookies just didn't taste very good, though, and neither did the lemonade.

George and Tim had a queer, uncomfortable feeling inside. The uncomfortable feeling kept getting bigger and bigger. Finally it seemed as if there wasn't much of anything left in them but a big uncomfortableness.

George cleared his throat and said, "I guess it wouldn't be much fun to have to sit in a wheel chair all the time."

Tim looked out at the warm spring day and replied, "No, it wouldn't. It would be awful not to be able to swim or play ball or climb trees or even—walk."

Then they looked at each other and walked quietly into the kitchen. "Mom," George said, looking at the floor, "Tim and I thought we might as well take those cookies——"

"Oh!" said Mother. "I'm sorry, but I just slipped over there with them myself."

The boys looked quite disappointed.

"Maybe we could take her something else," Tim said. "I have ten cents."

"I have money in my bank," George added. "We could get her a doll or——"

"Yes," agreed Tim. "She likes dolls."

"Why not just pay her a call today?" Mother said with a funny little smile.

A lady answered their knock next door. "We—we've come to see Frances," George said, feeling his face getting red. "I'm George from next door, and this is my friend Tim."

"Come right in, boys," the lady said. "Fran will be glad to see you."

She led the way to the room where Fran was sitting in a wheel chair. The chair was facing the windows with its back to the door. "Fran," she said, "here are George from next door, and his friend Tim."

The newcomer looked around.

George and Tim stared open-mouthed at a boy who sat in a chair.

"Hi!" said Fran with a smile. "It was nice of your mother to bring the cookies."

"We're lucky to have such fine neighbors," Fran's mother said as she left the room.

Beside Fran was the big basket of "dolls" that the boys had seen the moving men carry into the house.

"I'm fixing my puppets," Fran explained. "They got all tangled up in moving."

"Puppets!" exclaimed George and Tim at the very same time.

Fran showed the boys how to move the puppets by the strings attached to their arms and legs. "I can put on real plays with them in my puppet theater over there," he said.

George and Tim went nearer to the little theater. "Look," said Tim. "It has curtains and scenery and even electric lights."

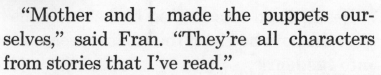

"Mother and I made the puppets ourselves," said Fran. "They're all characters from stories that I've read."

"Here's Daniel Boone," said George. "It would be fun to make him do things."

"I felt pretty bad when I found out I had to be in a wheel chair all winter," said Fran. "Then Mom and Dad thought of puppets to keep me busy. I'll be out of my wheel chair soon, but I've had so much fun with the puppets that I'll never give them up."

"I should say not!" agreed Tim.

"I'd like to learn how to make them work," said George.

"I'll show both of you if you want me to," Fran offered. "How about tomorrow?"

"Fine," said George. "It's Saturday, and we won't have to go to school."

"You know," said Fran, "I hated to leave my friends back home, but Mother said I'd make friends here soon. Sure enough, here you are on the first day!"

"We're glad we came," said Tim.

"I'm glad you moved in next door to me," said George. "It's going to be great to have another boy living on this street."

WOULD YOU BELIEVE?

THE FLOOGLES HAVE THEIR
PICTURE TAKEN

The Floogles are very nice people. There are Mr. Floogle and Mrs. Floogle and Amos Floogle and Fanny Flora Floogle and the dog, Snitkin Floogle. Everybody likes the Floogles. If only they weren't always getting so confused—like the time the photographer visited them.

He was a very old photographer, and his camera was as heavy as it was old. When he saw Mr. Floogle cheerfully raking the grass, the old photographer called across the fence, "Sir, the road is dusty and the camera heavy. May I have a drink of water before I walk on into town?"

"Come in! Come in!" cried Mr. Floogle.

Mrs. Floogle sniffed. "Water, indeed! Bring him into my kitchen for a glass of milk."

So there was a flurry and a scurry while Amos sliced ham for a sandwich—and cut his finger, of course. Fanny Flora got out a plate of fresh-baked cookies. Mr. Floogle cut the cheese and Mrs. Floogle poured the milk and Snitkin sat up and begged.

"Well," said the old photographer. "Well!"

When he'd finished his fine lunch, he eased his belt to a comfortable notch and said, "Now I will do a kindness for you. I will take your picture, a fine family picture."

The Floogles were as excited as bluejays. It would be wonderful. It would be splendid. They would send the picture to Aunt Hepzibah Floogle—no, to Cousin Ermintrude Floogle—perhaps to Big Grandfather Floogle. Well, that could be decided later.

All the while the old photographer grew more and more sleepy. The day, you know, was warm, the lunch had been good, and the old man was older than his camera.

"Come along now," said Mrs. Floogle. "It's time we had our picture taken."

The old photographer arranged the Floogles carefully, with Snitkin in front since he was the smallest. Then the old man pulled the black cloth over his head and was ready.

Mr. Floogle said, "Oh, this will not do! Fanny Flora should be in front, for our Aunt Hepzibah will want to see how very nicely her pretty curls swing."

So Fanny Flora stood in front and Snitkin sat beside her. Then the old man put the black cloth over his head and was ready.

Mrs. Floogle said, "Oh, this will not do either. Big Grandfather will want to see how straight Amos's teeth have grown in."

So Amos stood in front, too, and Snitkin sat in the middle. Then the old man pulled the black cloth over his head and was ready.

Fanny Flora said, "This will not do at all! Cousin Ermintrude will want to see Mama's beautiful new dress with the morning-glories and yellow buttons way down to the hem."

By this time the old photographer was so sleepy that he could not keep even one eye open. "I'll just rest a minute," he said, "while you make up your minds." He sank into Mr. Floogle's own comfortable chair and at once was snoring gently and politely.

At last the Floogles made up their minds. Everybody was to stand in front. Then all the relatives could see how nicely Fanny Flora's curls swung; how straight Amos's teeth had grown in; how beautiful Mrs. Floogle's morning-glory dress was; and how wonderfully Mr. Floogle's gold watch looped on its chain across his vest.

"It is too bad to wake the old man," said Mrs. Floogle. "He seems so tired."

"We needn't call him," said Amos Floogle, who had once found a broken Brownie and therefore knew all about cameras. "You take the picture by pinching the little bulb on that cord. I think the cord is long enough so that I can be in the picture and take it, too."

It was, too.

"Now I'll peek under the black cloth," said Amos, "and see what our picture looks like before I pinch the bulb."

So Amos Floogle peeked under the black cloth. "My goodness!" he cried. "This is terrible. We are upside down!"

"Let me see," said Mr. Floogle. He peeked under the black cloth. "We are indeed upside down," he went on, shaking his head.

"Oh, dear!" said Mrs. Floogle. "I don't mind so much for myself. I've lived a long time without a picture and I can live longer if need be, but the old photographer was being so nice. It is a sad thing to disappoint him. We must think of something to do."

So the Floogles thought and thought—in their confused way of thinking.

"If the camera takes pictures upside down——" said Mr. Floogle.

"And we want our picture right side up——" said Amos Floogle.

"Then we must——" said Fanny Flora.

"If Fanny Flora and I want our faces to be clear, we must——" said Mrs. Floogle.

"Of course," said Amos Floogle.

"Naturally," said Mr. Floogle.

"And Snitkin?" asked Fanny Flora.

"Snitkin cannot be in this picture, I am afraid," decided Mr. Floogle.

So the Floogles got ready and Amos said, "Hup!" just for practice and peeked under the black cloth. "As right as rain," he said as he took his place in the picture, keeping the long cord and the little bulb handy.

"One, two, three, hup!" said Mr. Floogle, and Amos pinched the little bulb.

"There!" said all the Floogles happily.

The shadows were long and the robins noisy when the old photographer woke from his dreaming. "Your picture!" he cried.

The Floogles gave him supper and told him not to worry, for they had taken care of the picture all by themselves. Then the old man went into the barn and developed the picture. He was so puzzled with the picture he got that the Floogles had to explain.

"But people always look upside down in a camera like this," the photographer said.

When he had wiped the tears of laughter from his eyes, he took a proper picture of the Floogles. He also promised to make enough copies for Aunt Hepzibah and Cousin Ermintrude and Big Grandfather and Little Grandmother. And he did.

Of course, the Floogles like better the picture they took while the old man was sleeping. They keep it on top of the piano with a lace

doily under it. Their friends look at it and look at it, for it is very unusual.

"Hold it so that the Floogles are standing and the table and chairs all hang from the ceiling," say their friends. "Hold it so that the table and chairs are on the floor properly and the Floogles are hanging by their toes. It is very confusing."

It is confusing, but the Floogles have all promised that they will never, never, NEVER tell they were so confused that they stood on their heads to take their own picture.

EXTREMES

I

A little boy once played so loud
That the Thunder, up in a thunder-cloud,
Said, "Since *I* can't be heard, why, then
I'll never, never thunder again!"

II

And a little girl once kept so still
That she heard a fly on the window-sill
Whisper and say to a ladybird—
"She's the stilliest child I ever heard."

FIRST CHILD ON MARS

"I want to go to Earth *now!*" Martia cried. She stamped her foot, although she was nine years old and knew better.

Martia Kendrick had dark shiny eyes and wore her hair in two short pigtails with bows at the ends. Usually she was smiling, but now she was not. Her mother gave her a warning look, but said only, "Now eat your protein pill and finish up your stewed clover."

Martia pushed at the food with her fork and took a bite or two. Breakfast on Mars was much like every other meal. The people there ate whatever they could raise on Mars itself. It was too expensive to bring food from Earth by rocket ship.

You see, Martia was born on Mars and had never been to Earth. Still, she had learned a lot about Earth from books and from the lessons her mother gave her.

Before Earth people had come to Mars, there had been only plants and a few insects there. Even now, there were no dogs or cats for Martia to play with, and there were no other children. All the other people were grown-up scientists who had come to study rocks, insects, and plants.

Mars was a strange place for Earth people to live. It was much colder than Earth, for it was farther from the sun, and there was very little air to hold the heat. Martia and the other people on Mars had to wear heavy warm coveralls, like snowsuits.

The air on Mars was so thin that the Martian sky was dark purplish blue, with hardly a cloud and never a rainstorm. This was nice, but there was not enough oxygen in this air for people to be able to breathe freely.

Everyone had to live and work within a huge plastic dome filled with good air. If someone went outside the dome, he had to pass through a great double door, called an airlock. Oh, how Martia wanted to go to Earth where people went outdoors without thinking about how to get enough air to breathe! Martia knew, though, that she could not go to Earth now.

Her father and mother were both doctors. They had come to Mars to find a cure for Mars fever. This fever was not serious, but it made Earth people very uncomfortable for weeks at a time. Worst of all, people could get it again and again.

Martia knew that her parents couldn't go to Earth until they had found a cure for Mars fever. Finding a cure might take years.

Just as Martia was wondering what an Earth breakfast would taste like, the phone rang. Father answered it and came back with a worried look. "Some more people have become sick with Mars fever—and today I was to go to the rocket landing field to get our supplies!"

Then Mother said, "It would be too bad to spoil the surprise you were planning for Martia today. I'll look after the sick people while you and Martia go to the field."

"Surprise?" Martia said happily. She hugged her mother to thank her for staying home so that she and Father could go.

At the airlock Martia and her father put on their oxygen masks and went outside the dome. A special car took them to the jet plane, which would carry them to the rocket port six hundred miles away. The rocket port had been built far away so that the fiery blasts would not damage the colony.

Of course the trip by jet plane did not take long. It just seemed long to Martia, because she could hardly wait for the surprise.

As they flew along, Martia thought about how different Mars was from Earth. There

were no mountains, or real trees, or wide roll-
ing hills. There were no lakes or rivers.

Even in the big Mars swamps you could not
see the water, for there was just enough to
make the ground muddy and squishy. Most
of the remaining land was nothing but sand
and rock.

When the jet came in at the landing field,
a giant rocket ship stood there pointing its
silver nose at the dark purple sky. "Some day,"
thought Martia, "I'll get in such a rocket ship
and zoom down to Earth."

Martia and her father went into a small dome on the field to wait for the supplies to be taken off the rocket ship. A small closed-in tractor brought the supplies from the ship to the dome. There was only one small box on the tractor for Martia's father.

"Here's the surprise," he said, opening the box so Martia could look inside. Martia peeked in. Then she squealed with delight. There were four furry little animals!

"Guinea pigs," said Father. "These will help us find a cure for Mars fever." Then he went on to explain that he and Mother would test the fever on the little animals and try many possible cures. This would be faster and safer than trying out cures on people.

Martia patted one of the guinea pigs.

"Would you like to have that one?" Father asked. "You may keep him as a pet."

All the way back home on the jet plane she held the fuzzy little animal in her arms. By the time Mother saw him, Martia had named him Benjamin, or "Benjy" for short.

For a week after that Martia forgot about going to Earth. She was too busy playing with Benjy and showing him to her grown-up

friends, especially to Professor Heron, who was her very best friend.

Professor Heron studied the strange plants on Mars. He had a garden where he grew these Martian plants.

Martia began to take Benjy over to Professor Heron's house every day. Then one morning when she went in to awaken Benjy and feed him, she found him whimpering and snuffling badly. He wouldn't eat his fresh Mars clover, and his nose was hot and dry.

Martia's heart sank. Poor Benjy had Mars fever. Now Father would probably take him away and try some cures on him!

Martia decided that she would try to help Benjy herself before her father came home from work. Then she had another idea. Maybe Professor Heron would know what to do. She put Benjy inside her jacket and held him there as she raced over to the professor's garden.

When the professor saw Benjy he said, "Humm, I don't know. Plants are my business. Now if you had a sick plant, I could tell you what you would have to do."

Martia felt all tight inside, as though she might cry. So the professor said, "Well, don't worry. At least we can make little Benjy more comfortable than he is now."

Together they put Benjy in a little box and covered him with a cloth to keep him warm. "Now I've often found that when you can't figure out a problem right away, it's best to think of something else for a while," he said.

He took Martia's hand and they walked through his garden. "Do you remember what this plant is?" he said. He was pointing to a patch of clover that looked like Mars clover— but Martia knew it was not.

"It's poison clover," Martia answered. Martia knew the professor was trying to change her thoughts to cheer her up, but it didn't help. She kept thinking of Benjy.

"Right you are," the professor was saying. "Poison clover grows in marshes right next to the good clover, and the men who go out to gather our food have to be watchful that they don't get the wrong kind."

They were walking on slowly when suddenly the professor cried, "Stop him!"

Benjy had left his box and hopped across the path to the poison clover. He was nibbling on it! Martia screamed and ran to him.

The professor looked worried. "Martia, you'd better take Benjy home now where he won't get into any more poison plants."

Martia spent the rest of the day looking after Benjy and worrying about him. Still, he didn't seem to feel any worse.

POISON CLOVER

Dr. Kendrick worked late that night, so Martia didn't tell him about Benjy. The next morning when Martia woke up, Benjy hopped out of his box to meet her. He seemed as bright and frisky as ever. His nose was moist and pink. In fact, he seemed well!

Yet how could he be well so soon, when it took people weeks and weeks to recover?

Then Martia remembered something. Benjy had eaten the poison clover, and no human being would think of doing that. Suppose there was something in that bad clover that made you well when you had Mars fever? Martia decided to tell Professor Heron.

The professor scratched his head and looked long and hard at Benjy. "Of course," he said finally, "there are other juices besides the poison in that clover. We'll tell your father and he can see whether the clover cures other sick guinea pigs."

Then he went on, "It will mean lots of work for your parents, but if they can prove that the poison clover works, they will have made the biggest discovery on Mars. People will no longer suffer from Mars fever."

Martia's father and mother spent many weeks testing the poison clover. There was much hard work and staying up late at night. Then, at last, they proved that a part of the poison clover did cure the fever. The good news was sent back to Earth, and from Earth came even better news for Martia.

The Kendrick family could leave Mars.

At last the day came. Mother and Father and Martia went through the airlock and flew to the rocket port for the last time. As they zoomed away in the rocket ship, Martia waved good-by to the planet Mars—but not to her little pet Benjy. He was snuggled close inside her jacket, going to Earth.

THE FLYING GINGERBREAD

Many years ago on New Year's Eve, Fritz, a baker of New Amsterdam, took the last tray of gingerbread men out of the oven. Then he shut the iron oven door on the glowing coals. The bake shop was very dark.

Fritz lit a candle to look at his wonderful gingerbread men—fat, well browned, and good smelling. He had just made up the recipe for these funny brown cakes and had refused to give it to the other bakers.

He, Fritz, would be the only baker in New Amsterdam with gingerbread men to sell for New Year's gifts. He could almost hear all the pennies clinking into his hands tomorrow.

Then he looked at the cuckoo clock on the wall and forgot about pennies. It was way past eleven o'clock, and New Year's Eve was nearly as bad for witches as Halloween! Would he be safe in the bake shop until midnight?

Fritz watched the minutes tick tock, tick tock slowly away. If he had gone home earlier he might have walked with the butcher or the candlestick maker whose shops were near by. Instead, he had stayed in his shop to bake more and more gingerbread.

The clock made a whirring sound. Now the cuckoo would pop out and sing for midnight. Fritz felt safe already. Then the clock's whir broke off in a frightened gasp. The cuckoo hid inside the clock. The candle flickered.

Through the locked door—through the locked door of the bake shop came—a witch! She was even more frightful than Fritz had imagined a witch could be.

"Give me a dozen of your gingerbread men," she screamed at Fritz.

Give away twelve gingerbread men? Lose twelve pennies? Fritz hesitated.

"Be quick about it!" The witch stamped her foot angrily. "A dozen, I said."

Fritz reached for the gingerbread men. He tried to pick out the least fat and the least nicely browned. Counting twelve, he reached for a sheet of paper to wrap them.

"A dozen, I said!" the witch screamed.

"Twelve is a dozen," Fritz said, trembling.

"Thirteen! I'll take no less!" the witch screamed on. "Thirteen is a baker's dozen."

That was too much. Fritz yelled back at her, "Give thirteen to the dozen? Never! Nothing can make me do it!"

"You won't? Nothing can make you? We'll see about that!" the witch cried out.

Crash-h-h-h! Off she went on her broom again, through the locked door of the shop.

Shakily, Fritz placed the twelve gingerbread men back on the shelf. Once again the candle burned clearly. The cuckoo peeped around the little carved door of the clock. Then it came out and cuckooed twelve times for midnight. Fritz wondered whether he had fallen asleep and had a bad dream.

When Fritz opened the bake shop the next morning, he felt that something was wrong. He went to get the gingerbread men to place in the shop window. The children would see them there and come in to buy things.

Then he blinked. He shook his head and blinked again. The shelves were empty.

"I've been robbed!" Fritz cried, running from the shop. "Stop, thief!"

The butcher and the candlestick maker came hurrying from their shops. "A thief, Fritz? What did he steal?"

"My beautiful gingerbread men!" Fritz turned to show them. "Gone! All gone——" Just then he stopped, open-mouthed.

The gingerbread men were flying through the open door of the bake shop. Light as feathers, they had been bobbing near the ceiling ready to float out the door.

Fritz ran to catch them. When he stretched on tiptoe to reach one, the gingerbread man

163

floated away. Fritz ran to another. Brushing his fingers, it floated higher. Fritz rushed here! He leaped there! Still, he could not reach a single one.

Just then Peter Van Loon came around the corner. When Peter saw the flying ginger-bread men, he leaped high in the air. The brownest and fattest gingerbread man settled down into his waiting hands.

"Oh Gretchen! Heinrich! Dirk! Everyone, hurry! hurry!" Peter called. "Here is ginger-bread, free for the catching!"

Children came running, and the ginger-bread men floated down into their hands. When Fritz asked them for pennies, the rest of the gingerbread men sailed away down the street. The funny cakes seemed to want the children to run after them.

Fritz was a stubborn man. "I will bake more gingerbread men," he said. "I will make a heavier batter. The next gingerbread men will not be light enough to fly."

They weren't, either! The next ones were so heavy they broke through the oven onto the floor. Fritz mixed another batch. These flew up the chimney! He tried again. These

gingerbread men ran around inside the oven like little mice.

Fritz gave in then. "I will give thirteen to the dozen," he shouted.

Fritz heard the witch laugh. At once the little gingerbread men who were running around in the oven came out and climbed up on the shelves.

Fritz was even better than his word. He gave thirteen to the dozen so willingly that a "baker's dozen" has meant "more than enough" ever since. Best of all, if a child without a penny flattened his nose longingly against Fritz's shop window, he was sure to get a fine gingerbread man—free.

THE OWL AND THE PUSSY CAT

The Owl and the Pussy Cat went to sea
  In a beautiful pea-green boat:
They took some honey, and plenty of money
  Wrapped up in a five-pound note.
The Owl looked up to the stars above,
  And sang to a small guitar,
"O lovely Pussy, O Pussy, my love,
What a beautiful Pussy you are,
      You are,
      You are!
What a beautiful Pussy you are!"

Pussy said to the Owl, "You elegant fowl,
   How charmingly sweet you sing!
Oh! let us be married; too long we have
      tarried:
   But what shall we do for a ring?"
They sailed away, for a year and a day,
   To the land where the bong-tree grows;
And there in a wood a Piggy-wig stood,
   With a ring at the end of his nose,
            His nose,
            His nose,
With a ring at the end of his nose.

"Dear Pig, are you willing to sell for one
      shilling
   Your ring?" Said the Pig, "I will."
So they took it away, and were married next
      day
   By the Turkey who lives on the hill.
They dined on mince and slices of quince,
   Which they ate with a runcible spoon;
And hand in hand, on the edge of the sand,
   They danced by the light of the moon,
            The moon,
            The moon,
They danced by the light of the moon.

SOME OF MY FATHER'S ADVENTURES

When my father was a small boy, an alley cat told him about a jungle island where a dragon lived. My father packed a knapsack with all kinds of things and went to the jungle to find the dragon.

At last he came out into a clearing and ran right into the middle of it so that he could see anything that might try to attack him. Was he surprised when he looked and saw fourteen green eyes coming out of the jungle all around the clearing, and when the green eyes turned into seven tigers!

The tigers walked around him in a big circle, looking hungrier all the time. Then they sat down and began to talk.

"I suppose you thought we didn't know you were trespassing in our jungle!"

Then the next tiger spoke. "I suppose you're going to say you didn't know it was our jungle!"

"Did you know that not one explorer has ever left this island alive?" said the third tiger in an angry voice.

The tigers went on talking in turn. "You're
our first little boy, you know. I'm curious
to know if you're especially tender."

"Maybe you think we have regular meal-
times, but we don't. We just eat whenever
we're hungry," said the fifth tiger.

"And we're very hungry right now. In
fact, I can hardly wait," said the sixth.

"I can't wait!" said the seventh tiger.

Then all the tigers said together in a loud
roar, "Let's begin right now!" At this they
moved in closer.

My father looked at those seven hungry
tigers, and then he had an idea. He quickly
opened his knapsack and took out some chew-

ing gum, which was very scarce on the island. He threw them each a piece but they only growled, "As fond as we are of chewing gum, we're sure we'd like you better!"

"But this is very special chewing gum," said my father. "If you keep on chewing it long enough it will turn green, and then if you plant it, it will grow more chewing gum, and the sooner you start chewing the sooner you'll have more."

The tigers said, "Why, you don't say! Isn't that fine!" And as each one wanted to be the first to plant the chewing gum, they all unwrapped their pieces and began chewing as hard as they could. Every once in a while one tiger would look into another's mouth and say, "Nope, it isn't done yet."

Finally they were all so busy looking into each other's mouths to make sure that no one was getting ahead that they forgot about being hungry.

My father soon found a trail leading away from the clearing. He hadn't gone very far when he heard an angry animal roaring, "Ding blast it! I told you not to go blackberrying yesterday. Won't you ever learn?"

My father crept along and peered into a small clearing just ahead. A lion was prancing about clawing at his mane, which was all snarled and full of blackberry twigs. The more he clawed the worse it became and the madder he grew and the more he yelled at himself, because it was himself he was yelling at all the time.

My father could see that the trail went through the clearing, so he decided to crawl around the edge in the underbrush and not disturb the lion.

He crawled and crawled, and the yelling grew louder and louder. Just as he was about to reach the trail on the other side, the yelling stopped. My father looked around and saw the lion glaring at him.

"Who are you?" the lion yelled.

"My name is Elmer Elevator."

"Where do you think you're going?"

"I'm going home," said my father.

"That's what you think!" said the lion. "Ordinarily I'd save you for afternoon tea, but I happen to be upset enough and hungry enough to eat you right now." And he picked up my father in his front paws to feel how fat he was.

My father said, "Oh, please, Lion, before you eat me, tell me why you are so particularly upset today."

"It's my mane," said the lion, as he was figuring how many bites a little boy would make. "You see what a dreadful mess it is, and I don't seem to be able to do anything about it. But I'm going to eat you now, so it won't make any difference to you."

"Oh, wait a minute," said my father, "and I'll give you just the things you need to make

172

your mane all tidy and beautiful. I have them here in my pack."

"You do?" said the lion. "Well, give them to me, and perhaps I'll save you for afternoon tea after all." Then he put my father down on the ground.

My father opened the pack and took out a comb and brush and seven hair ribbons of different colors. "Look," he said. "I'll show you what to do on your forelock, where you can watch me. First you brush a while, and then you comb, and then you brush again until all the twigs and snarls are gone. Then you divide it in three and braid it and tie a ribbon around the end."

As my father was doing this, the lion watched very carefully and began to look much happier. When my father tied on the ribbon, the lion was all smiles. "Oh, that's wonderful, really wonderful!" he exclaimed. "Let me have the comb and brush to see whether I can do it."

So my father gave him the comb and brush, and the lion began busily grooming his mane. As a matter of fact, he was so busy that he didn't even know when my father left.

173

TALK

One day a farmer went to his garden to dig up some yams. While he was digging, one of the yams said to him, "Well, at last you're here. You never weeded me, but now you come around with your digging stick. Go away!"

The farmer turned and looked at his cow in amazement. The cow was chewing her cud and looking at him. "Did you say something?" the man asked his cow.

The cow kept on chewing and said nothing, but the man's dog spoke up and answered him. "It was the yam who spoke to you," the dog said. "Listen to what the yam says."

From *The Cow-Tail Switch and Other West African Stories* by Harold Courlander and George Herzog. Copyright, 1947, Henry Holt and Company, Inc.

The man became angry, because his dog had never talked before. Besides, he didn't like the dog's tone. He took his knife and cut a branch from a tree to whip the dog. Just then the tree said, "Put that branch down."

The man was getting very upset. He started to throw the branch away, but the branch said, "Man, put me down softly."

The man put the branch down gently on a stone, and the stone said, "Hey, take that thing off me!"

Now the frightened farmer started to run to the village. On the road he met a fisherman with a fish trap on his head.

"What's the hurry?" the fisherman asked.

The farmer said, "My yam said, 'Go away!' Then the dog said, 'Listen to what the yam says!' When I cut a branch to whip the dog, the tree said, 'Put that branch down!' The branch said, 'Do it softly!' Then the stone said, 'Take that thing off me!'"

"Is that all?" the man with the fish trap asked. "Is that so frightening?"

"Well," the man's fish trap said, "did he take it off the stone?"

"Wah!" the fisherman shouted. He threw

175

his fish trap on the ground and began to run with the farmer. On the road they met a weaver with a bundle of cloth on his head. "Where are you going in such a rush?" the weaver asked.

"My yam said, 'Go away!' " the farmer said. "The dog said, 'Listen to what the yam says!' The tree said, 'Put that branch down!' The branch said, 'Do it softly!' And the stone said, 'Take that thing off me!' "

"And then," the fisherman continued, "the fish trap said, 'Did he take it off?' "

"That's nothing to get excited about," the weaver said, "nothing at all."

"Oh, yes, it is," the bundle of cloth said. "If it happened to you, you'd run."

"Wah!" shouted the weaver. Then he threw his bundle on the road and started running, too. The men came to the river, where they found a man swimming.

The swimmer looked at the frightened men. "Are you chasing a deer?" he asked.

The first man said breathlessly, "My yam talked to me. It said, 'Go away!' And my dog said, 'Listen to your yam!' When I cut myself a branch, the tree said, 'Put that branch down!' The branch said, 'Do it softly!' And the stone said, 'Take that thing off me!' "

The fisherman panted, "And then my fish trap said, 'Did he?' "

The weaver wheezed, "And my bundle of cloth said, 'You'd run, too.' "

"Is that why you're running?" the man in the river asked.

"Well, wouldn't you run if you were in their shoes?" the river asked.

The swimmer jumped out of the water and began to run with the other men. They all ran down the main street of the village to the

house of the judge. The judge's servant brought out a stool, and the judge sat on it to listen to the men's troubles.

"I went to my garden to dig yams," the farmer said, waving his arms. "Then everything began to talk. My yam said, 'Go away!' My dog said, 'Listen to your yam!' The tree said, 'Put that branch down!' The branch said, 'Do it softly!' And the stone said, 'Take that thing off me!' "

"And my fish trap said, 'Well, did he take it off?' " the fisherman said.

"And my cloth said, 'You'd run, too!' " the weaver said.

"The river said the same thing," the swimmer said in a hoarse voice.

The judge listened patiently, but he could not keep from scowling. "Now this really is a wild story," he said at last. "You'd better go back to your work before I find you guilty of disturbing the peace."

The men went away, and the judge shook his head and mumbled to himself, "Nonsense like that upsets the whole village."

"Unbelievable, isn't it?" his stool said. "Imagine, a talking yam!"

LOOKING AROUND YOU

BEN'S GREAT EXPERIMENT

Many years ago, a certain gentleman by the name of Benjamin Franklin decided to try a dangerous experiment. He would need a kite for the experiment, but a paper kite would not do. This kite would have to fly in the wind and wet of a thunderstorm.

For a long time Mr. Franklin had been wondering about lightning. What was it? Could it be brought out of the clouds down to earth?

No one knew about these things at that time. People were terribly afraid of lightning. They thought the flashes of fire meant that God was angry with them.

Ben Franklin didn't believe this. He thought lightning was electric fire, and he proposed to bring this fire down to earth with his kite to prove that he was right.

He made a cross of two light strips of wood and fastened a large silk handkerchief to the four ends. Then he fastened a sharp-pointed wire to the top of the upright stick. The wire rose a foot or more above the wood.

The kite had a tail, loop, and string just like other kites. The string was cotton twine.

To the end of the twine Mr. Franklin tied a silk ribbon, which he would hold in his hand. Where the twine and silk ribbon joined, he tied a small metal key.

Mr. Franklin believed the pointed wire would draw electric fire from the clouds. He also thought this fire would run down to the metal key as soon as the kite and twine were wet. If he was right, he would get a strong electric shock when he touched the key.

The silk ribbon must be kept dry all the time or he might get a shock that would kill

him. He was taking a great risk, even with the ribbon dry. Nevertheless, he was determined to try the experiment.

The kite was now ready. He had only to wait for the lightning—and one day it came.

The sky was black with thunderclouds when Mr. Franklin went out into a field with his kite. He stood under a shed to keep the silk ribbon dry, and he was careful that the twine did not touch the door frame. He wanted the current to flow freely to the key. It must not be stopped in any way.

Now the black clouds were right over the kite. If he could bring electric fire down, he must do it as soon as the lightning flashed through the sky again.

The thunder roared! The lightning flashed! Then came the rain. Mr. Franklin touched the key with his knuckles. At once he received a strong shock, and the key gave off sparks of electric fire. Again and again he touched the key, and each time he felt the shock and saw the fiery sparks.

He was delighted. He had proved his idea! He had brought electric fire out of the clouds and down to the earth!

THE LIGHTHOUSE BELL

Boing! Boing! Benji stood in Gram's kitchen and covered his ears at the sound of the lighthouse bell. Gram laughed and said, "You'll get used to it, Benji. Gramp and I don't even hear the bell any more. Before your visit is over, you won't mind hearing it."

Benji was glad he had come to visit Gram and Gramp on the island. He knew he'd have fun. Still, he thought, "I'll never go to sleep tonight with the awful racket of that bell ringing every four minutes!"

Gram said, "You go out and look for Gramp. He's down by the tower. About this time every day he fills the gasoline tank on the generator inside the lighthouse."

"What's the generator?" asked Benji.

"Gramp will tell you," Gram replied.

Boing! Boing! Benji's ears ached with the sound of the bell. He stood for a minute on the front steps of the cottage and looked at the island and the sea wall around it.

Big and round, and glistening white in the bright sun, was the lighthouse tower. It rose high above the little island.

Benji shivered, staring at the top of the tower and at the sea gulls that were flying in

184

great, swooping circles. The tower seemed to reach to the very sky.

Boing! Boing! Gramp came out of the lighthouse, and Benji ran to him. "It's scary," he said, taking his grandfather's hand.

"Yes, it is, when you're not used to it," Gramp replied. "Now let's take care of that gasoline, shall we?"

Benji helped Gramp wheel a big barrel of gasoline into the room at the bottom of the tower. In the middle of the room there was a motor that was running.

"That gasoline motor drives the generator," Gramp said, "and the generator makes all the electricity we use here on the island. It makes the electricity for our lights and for working the hammer that bangs the bell. The same electricity lights the beacon on top of the tower at night and on foggy days."

Then Gramp and Benji started for the top of the tower. As they climbed the stone steps, Gramp explained that the building was made like two towers, one inside the other. The steps wound around, up and up, between the two walls. Gramp and Benji stopped to rest at each full turn.

Boing! Boing! Inside the tower the sound of the bell was faint and low. The stairs were dark, for the only light came through small glass windows. They were solid white with salt spray from the ocean.

The climb was a tough one. Benji and Gramp were out of breath when they reached the top of the stairs. Here, Gramp pushed on the ceiling. A trap door swung up and they climbed into the bell room.

Gramp reached up and pulled down the handle of a switch. "We'll shut off the bell for eight minutes," he said. "If it bonged while we were up here, it would almost deafen us."

The bell was nearly as big as the round room in which they stood. It hung from a huge wooden beam. Beside it, in a box, was some machinery. Gramp showed Benji how the hammer made the great bell ring.

Going to one side of the bell room, Gramp pointed out across the water. Benji saw a huge boat wallowing slowly up and down in the waves. "There goes a tramp steamer, out-bound," Gramp said. The boat hardly seemed to move, but black smoke came from its stack, and the water behind was filled with bubbles.

"How high up are we?" asked Benji.

"Sixty feet above the cottage, one hundred feet above low tide," answered Gramp.

"Whew, that's high, isn't it?"

Gramp nodded. "This used to be the highest light on the coast, but now it's just the oldest. The new lighthouses have foghorns and circling searchlights and radios. The bigger ships take another lane into the harbor now, but we're still needed. We warn tramp steamers and oilers and fishing boats to keep away from this rocky coast."

Gramp lifted the switch so that the bell would ring again. Then he and Benji went slowly down the long, winding stairs.

A few nights later, a storm came up. The wind howled around the corners of the cottage, and big waves pounded against the sea wall. Benji might have been scared, if it hadn't been for the bell. He fell asleep listening for the next time it would ring. *Boing! Boing!*

Then, in the middle of the night, Benji awoke with a start. What had awakened him? He listened and waited. He could hear nothing but the noise of the storm.

Suddenly he knew why he was awake. The bell was not ringing! He had grown so used to hearing it that the silence had made him awaken. Something was wrong with the bell.

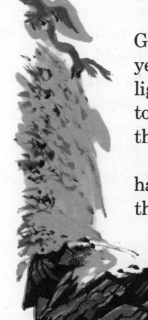

Benji ran to the kitchen in time to see Gramp standing at the door, buttoning his yellow slicker. He was saying to Gram, "Our lights are all right, so the trouble is up in the tower." As he opened the door, the sound of the storm was louder than ever.

"Gramp, wait——" said Gram, but Gramp had gone. Gram grabbed a small slicker from the hook back of the door and turned to Benji.

"Put this on and run," she said. "Run after Gramp and tell him not to hurry when he climbs the tower stairs. Tell him he must remember to climb slowly."

Outside, everything was black. Benji bent over as he ran, and the wind screamed over his head. The stones in the yard were wet, and he slipped and slid to the lighthouse. When he opened the heavy door, the wind almost tore it out of his grasp.

"Gramp!" Benji shouted. "Gram says not to hurry on the stairs." There was no answer, so Benji felt his way to the stairs and began to climb. He was afraid, because he never had been in the tower alone. The wind screamed as he climbed in the darkness, his hands feeling along the cold, rough wall. It was much farther to the top than he remembered.

"Gramp!" he called every few steps, but the roar of the wind and the waves made his voice sound weak and faint.

Benji felt a strong draft of air coming down toward him. Another turn of the stairs, and he saw a dull glow ahead. "What in the world are you doing here?" Gramp shouted as Benji climbed into the bell room.

Benji gave him Gram's message, and Gramp just snorted. Then he shouted, "Hold the flashlight for me while I find out what's wrong with this bell."

First Gramp pulled down the handle of the switch to turn off the current. In a moment he had opened the box that held the bell machinery. Then he began to poke around inside the box.

Benji held the light and looked. He saw a short wire that was hanging loose. "Is that wire supposed to be loose?" he asked.

"Where?" asked Gramp. Benji aimed the

light at the loose wire. Gramp said, "A-ha!" He took the end of the wire and fastened it to a place in the machinery.

"Now we'll see whether the bell will work," said Gramp, and he pulled up the handle of the switch. *Boing!* The bell worked.

Benji's head jerked back with the awful ear-splitting closeness of the sound. Gramp grinned and slapped him on the shoulder. Then they went down the stairs. The wind was as strong as ever when they crossed the yard, but Benji had Gramp's hand to hold onto tightly this time.

In the cottage, Gram had hot cocoa ready for them. Benji and Gramp changed to some dry clothes and came back to the kitchen to have some cocoa.

"Well, Gram," said Gramp. "Benji may have saved a ship tonight. He found what was wrong with the bell. It took courage for a fellow his size to go out in this storm and climb the tower alone in the dark."

Benji didn't say anything. He just sipped his cocoa and felt glad. *Boing! Boing!* The lighthouse bell seemed to echo Gramp's praise as it called out into the storm.

HOW BABY ANIMALS RIDE

Uncle Bim had just come home from a trip all around the world, and little Bob stood looking at him. "Tell me something about the places you visited," the boy said.

Uncle Bim smiled and invited Bob to sit on a stool near his chair. "Let's see," he said. "What would you like to hear?"

"Well, I'd like to hear about animals," Bob suggested quickly.

"Of course you would," said Uncle Bim, "and now I know just the story for you.

"One hot afternoon, over in Africa, I came upon a sparkling river. I stood for a moment looking at it, wondering whether it would be safe to go swimming there.

"Suddenly, out of the water came an ugly black head with little staring eyes. Then, very slowly, up came a fat black body with short legs. It was a baby hippopotamus, standing in the middle of the river."

"Standing on top of the water? How could he do that?" asked Bob.

"I wondered that, too," laughed Uncle Bim. "Probably I stood there with my mouth open

for a while. Then, very slowly, a mother hippo's back came out of the river and after that, her big black head.

"The mother hippo stared at me for a few minutes before she turned away. She swam down the river with big ripples following her. The baby hippo waggled his head and rode on her back, high and dry."

"I didn't know that hippos carried their babies on their backs," said Bob.

"Oh, quite a few animals do," said Uncle Bim. "In Australia, I saw a chubby, pug-nosed koala climbing a tree with her baby on her back. The baby's arms were wrapped around the mother's neck.

193

"Koalas live only in Australia," said Uncle
Bim. "They look much like bears."

Just then Bob's mother came into the room.
She had heard Uncle Bim talking, and sat
down to join in the conversation.

"I haven't traveled much," she said, "but
I've seen animals carrying their babies on
their backs. When I was your size, Bob, a
raccoon lived in the woods near us. I'll never
forget the time I saw her down by the creek.
She was standing at the water's edge with two
baby raccoons on her back."

"I saw an animal carrying its baby on its
back," said Bob. "It was a big white swan,
with a little swan's head sticking out of its

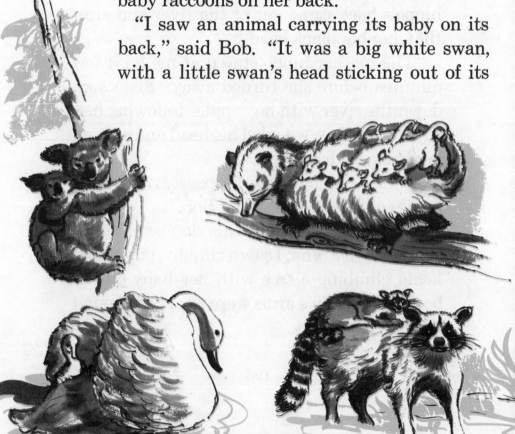

feathers. A swan is a bird, I know, but a bird is an animal, isn't it?"

"Yes," said Uncle Bim, "any living thing that isn't a plant is an animal."

"I've seen still another animal carrying babies on her back," said Mother. "Once I saw an opossum walking along a tree branch. Her long tail curled around in a sort of question mark, and on her back were three opossum children. Their tails reached up to their mother's tail and curled around it."

"That sounds even better than the jungle," said Uncle Bim. Then he took a shiny quarter from his pocket. "Bob," he said, "if you can name six animals that carry their babies on their backs, this quarter is yours."

"Six animals," said Bob. "Well, there are hippos, koalas, raccoons, swans, opossums, and—let's see——"

At that moment there was a sound at the top of the stairs. Bob's father was starting down with Bob's little sister on his shoulders. "I know!" Bob cried. "Hippos, koalas, raccoons, swans, opossums, and PEOPLE!"

Everybody laughed, and Uncle Bim handed Bob his shiny quarter.

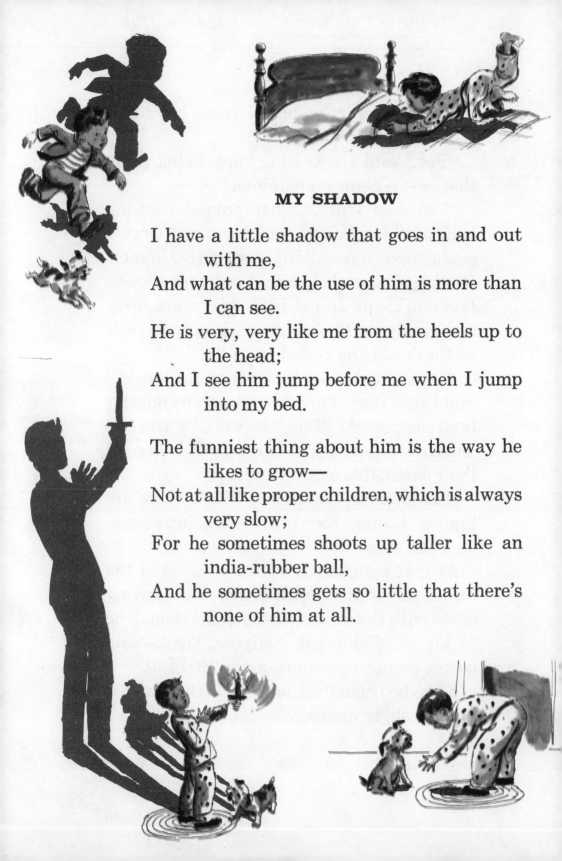

MY SHADOW

I have a little shadow that goes in and out
    with me,
And what can be the use of him is more than
    I can see.
He is very, very like me from the heels up to
    the head;
And I see him jump before me when I jump
    into my bed.

The funniest thing about him is the way he
    likes to grow—
Not at all like proper children, which is always
    very slow;
For he sometimes shoots up taller like an
    india-rubber ball,
And he sometimes gets so little that there's
    none of him at all.

He hasn't got a notion of how children ought
    to play,
And can only make a fool of me in every sort
    of way.
He stays so close beside me, he's a coward you
    can see;
I'd think shame to stick to nursie as that
    shadow sticks to me!

One morning, very early, before the sun was
    up,
I rose and found the shining dew on every
    buttercup;
But my lazy little shadow, like an arrant
    sleepy-head,
Had stayed at home behind me and was fast
    asleep in bed.

THE POPCORN THAT DIDN'T POP

"Just look at that!" Kate exclaimed, taking the corn popper from the stove. "Every grain is little and hard and burned. I'm so ashamed! I told Jim if he'd come over we'd have buttered popcorn. No one can eat this!"

"Jim could pop his own corn," her brother Bob reminded her. "He grows popcorn in his own back yard, you know."

"He says he doesn't have time. He grows it to sell in the stores, and it's hard work. I wish he'd come over, though. Maybe he could tell me why this batch didn't pop."

"I'll call him," Bob said. "I'd like to know, too, why popcorn sometimes pops and sometimes doesn't."

Just then Jim walked into the kitchen and called out, "Hello, everybody!"

"Oh, Jim, I'm glad you're here! We're in trouble," Kate said. "I told you we'd have a bowl of buttered popcorn—but look at this!" She showed him the burned grains.

"Well, I grow popcorn and I brought you some that *will* pop. Try this." Jim handed Kate a small paper bag.

Kate poured out the burned popcorn, cleaned the popper and sprinkled some of the kernels from the paper bag into it. She shook the corn popper back and forth over the hot stove to keep the kernels moving. She laughed happily and kept the corn dancing as the hard little kernels exploded. With crackling pops, the corn turned into white, crisp balls that filled the corn popper to the lid.

"You know everything about popcorn, Jim. Why didn't my popcorn pop?" Kate asked.

"How old is your corn?" asked Jim.

"Oh, I bought it months and months ago."

"Where did you have it stored?" Jim asked.

"In this dish in the kitchen cupboard," Kate answered, wondering at all the questions.

"Did the dish have a tight cover?"

Kate laughed. "It wasn't covered at all," she said. "Why be that careful about a few handfuls of popcorn?"

"Kate, do you know what makes popcorn pop?" Jim asked seriously.

Kate became serious, too. "Why, heat, I guess. It doesn't pop until it gets hot."

Jim picked up a kernel and held it in his fingers. "Did you ever look inside a kernel of popcorn?" he asked.

"Oh, yes, when it pops open, all white and fluffy, that's the inside," said Kate.

Jim cracked one of the hard little kernels open and laid the halves on the table. "I mean before it is popped," he said. "Take a look at the inside of this kernel."

Kate ran to get her magnifying glass, and Jim placed the broken kernel under it. Kate leaned close and studied the small piece. "I can see little white spots in the center of the kernel. What are they?" she asked.

"They are tiny sacs, or bags," Jim explained. "Each sac has a tiny bit of water in it. Now, what happens when water is heated?"

Bob edged up for a look at the strange white sacs. "I know what happens to the water in our teakettle when it gets hot. It turns into steam," he said.

"What would happen if you stopped the spout of the teakettle?" Jim asked Bob.

"The teakettle would blow up, I guess. Our kitchen would be a mess if that happened!" Bob answered quickly.

Again Bob studied the broken kernel, and in a moment he shouted, "Oh, boy, I know what! The heat turns the water in the white sacs to steam. The steam pushes so hard that it breaks the sacs and explodes the kernel of popcorn. Then it pops inside out!"

"Why didn't my popcorn pop?" Kate asked again. "Why didn't the water in the sacs turn to steam and make the kernels explode?"

"You kept your popcorn in a warm, dry place for a long time, didn't you?" Jim asked.

"Y-e-s," Kate said slowly. "I guess the water evaporated the way it does in the birdbath. I can't see the water disappear there, but in a little while, the birdbath is empty. It goes away slowly in a vapor instead of steam. Did the water in my popcorn evaporate until there was none left to explode the kernels?"

Jim laughed. "You've solved the mystery. If there is no water in the white sacs, they can't explode and turn the kernels inside out. The popcorn can't pop!"

"Well, now we know why popcorn pops and why it doesn't pop," Bob said. "The next thing to do is to pop a big batch, soak it in butter, and have a feast!"

THE ANGEL CHIMES

"Oh, Philip Olaf! How beautiful they are! Your three, tiny, silver angels look as if they could fly and sing!"

Philip Olaf had been so busy smoothing the tip of the third angel's wing that he was startled by the gay voice of the Princess Barbette. She had slipped into the silver-smith's shop so quietly that Philip Olaf had not heard her coming.

Philip had meant the three silver angels as a surprise Christmas gift for Princess Barbette, but now it was too late to hide them. Instead, he turned to greet the king's daughter.

"Grandfather says these angels are my best work so far," said the fair-haired, blue-eyed boy to the little girl.

The princess turned to greet the Royal Silversmith who was working on a chalice, or large cup, of silver for the king.

"Yes," agreed the silversmith, "Philip has done well with the angels."

"If only they could fly about and make a little music," she sighed as she stroked the third angel's tiny wing. Then she ran out of the shop as quickly as she had come.

Had the princess realized that the angels were for her? She had wanted the angels to fly and to make music. How could Philip make them move about and sing? The boy thought of little else that day, for Christmas was only a week away.

"Grandfather, can you not make these angels fly and sing?" Philip begged the old silversmith. "You can do anything with silver. I have heard the king himself say so."

The silversmith smiled at his grandson lovingly. "Ah, Philip Olaf, you, too, will use flattery when you want me to make something. I'll see what I can do. Just now I cannot stop to play with your three angel children. I have so much to finish before Christmas."

Philip decided to make a silver candle

holder and decorate it with the three silver angels. Still, there was the question of how to make the angels fly and sing.

The next afternoon when Philip came into the shop, he watched his grandfather make a silver carrousel. This was a miniature merry-go-round that fitted over a sharp needle-like spindle. It would spin around if one gave it a little push.

Suddenly Philip knew how he could make the angels fly. He, too, would make a minia-ture carrousel. Only he would fasten his silver

angels to the whirling circle instead of the silver horses that his grandfather had fastened to the tiny merry-go-round.

If only the angels could sing, too!

As he whirled them about, one of the angels' tiny feet struck the metal bar that supported the spindle. A sweet note sounded. Then Philip knew his angels could make music.

He fastened some little, hollow metal tubes to each angel, just where the angel was joined to the whirling circle. These tubes hung just below the angels. As they passed the spindle bar, the tubes tapped lightly on the metal and made sweet sounds. Now the silver angels could not only fly, they could sing!

On the base of the carrousel Philip fastened a little metal holder for the candles. There was one holder for each of the four corners. He decided to use red candles.

On Christmas Eve, Philip Olaf helped his grandfather put the shop in order. Every last piece of silver work was finished.

Then, at last, Philip brought out his candle holder for Princess Barbette. "See, Grandfather, it is all finished."

"Do the angels fly and sing?"

206

"They will fly when I push them," said the boy, "and they sing as they fly." He whirled the carrousel gaily.

"You have made them very well, Philip, and all by yourself. I am proud of your work. The princess will be delighted."

"You know, I do wish the angels could fly without my pushing them," Philip Olaf said as he looked at them thoughtfully.

The old silversmith examined the tiny candle holder carefully. He said knowingly, "Well, sometimes wonderful things happen on Christmas. Perhaps your angels will be able to fly and sing by themselves."

"A miracle, Grandfather?" asked Philip.

His grandfather would not say anything more except, "Do not light the candles until you give the carrousel to the princess."

When Philip Olaf carried the lovely little carrousel to Princess Barbette, she was very much pleased.

"Do the angels fly and sing?" she asked Philip hopefully.

"They do when I spin the carrousel," Philip said. "I will show you, but first let me light the candles."

Carefully, he lighted the four red candles, and the rosy glow seemed to bring life to the little silver angels. Then, as Philip watched, his eyes grew big with wonder.

As the warm air from the candles filled the hollow tubes, the silver angels began to move by themselves. At first they moved slowly, with the chimes tinkling only now and then. Soon, however, the carrousel began to move faster and faster. The flying angels were now singing all the time.

"It is indeed a miracle!" said Philip Olaf, and Princess Barbette nodded her head.

THE WONDERFUL WEAVER

There's a wonderful weaver
  High up in the air,
And he weaves a white mantle
  For cold earth to wear,
With the wind for his shuttle,
  The cloud for his loom,
How he weaves! How he weaves!
  In the light, in the gloom.

Oh! with finest of laces
  He decks bush and tree,
On the bare flinty meadows
  A cover lays he.
Then a quaint cap he places
  On pillar and post,
And he changes the pump
  To a grim, silent ghost.

But this wonderful weaver
  Grows weary at last,
And the shuttle lies idle
  That once flew so fast;
Then the sun peeps abroad
  On the work that is done;
And he smiles: "I'll unravel
  It all just for fun!"

SPEED

Once there was a beautiful white ox. His back was broad, his horns were long, and his eyes were large and gentle. As he walked slowly along the road one day he thought, "I am much pleased with myself—so large and strong am I. What would the world do without me?"

Just then he heard something coming *clopperty, clopperty, clopperty* down the road behind him. Up dashed a big black horse.

"Greetings," lowed the ox. "Why are you in such haste, my brother?"

The horse tossed his mane. "I'm in a hurry," he snorted, "because I'm made to go fast. Why, I can go ten miles while you crawl one! The world has no more use for a great white snail like you. If you want speed, I'm what you need. Watch how fast I go!"

The ox watched the horse disappear and he thought, "Surely this swift horse is much more wonderful than I!"

Now as the horse ran along he was thinking, "I am pleased with myself. I am sleek, and I

Adapted from *Here and Now Storybook* by Lucy Sprague Mitchell. Copyright 1921 by E. P. Dutton & Co., Inc. Renewal 1949 by Lucy Sprague Mitchell. Reprinted by permission of the publishers.

am swift—swifter than the ox. What would the world do without me?"

Just then he heard a strange humming overhead. He glanced up. The sound came from a vibrating wire. Then he heard fast-turning wheels coming *kathump, kathump.* A self-moving car, with a trolley touching the wire overhead, was coming along the road.

The horse was so scared that his eyes stuck out of his head and his mane stood on end. He wondered what made this thing go.

"Hello, clodhopper," yelled the electric car. "I didn't know there were any of you four-footed things left. Surely the world has no more use for you. Where you go in half a day,

I go in an hour. Where you carry one man, I carry ten. If you want speed, I'm what you need. Watch me!"

The horse watched the trolley car disappear, leaving only the humming wire overhead. He thought, "Surely this swift car is much more wonderful than I!"

Now the trolley went swinging on his way, thinking, "I am pleased with myself. My power is the same as the lightning that rips the sky. I am swifter than the big white ox, and swifter than the sleek black horse. What would the world do without me?"

Just then he heard a strange *chug, a-chug, a-chug, a-chug*. It sounded like a mighty monster coughing his life away! Then, to his

great horror, he saw a huge iron creature coming across the green field. Black smoke and fiery sparks were streaming from the creature's nose, which was on the top of his head!

"Well, slowpoke," screamed the engine as it came near the trolley car. "Out of breath? No wonder. You're not made to go fast the way I am, for I move by the great power of steam. Where you go in half a day, I go in an hour. If you want speed, I'm what you need. Good-by. Take your time, slow coach."

And *chug, a-chug, a-chug* he was off, leaving a trail of dirty smoke behind him. The poor trolley car thought, "Surely this ugly engine is much more wonderful than I!"

Now the engine raced down to the freight depot, which was near the shipping docks. As he waited to be loaded he thought, "I am pleased with myself. I am swifter than the ox, swifter than the horse, and swifter than the electric car. What would the world do without me? I serve everyone. I go everywhere——"

Just here he was interrupted by the deep and booming voice of a freight steamer lying alongside the wharf. The voice said, "*Tooot*, you funny landlubber! You go everywhere?

What about the water? Can you go to France and back again? It's only I who can haul the world's goods across the ocean!"

The speech made the steamer quite hoarse, so he cleared his throat with a long *toooot* and sank into silence.

"Of course, what he says is true," thought the engine. "At the same time, it is equally true that on land I do serve everyone, and I do go everywhere——"

Just here he was interrupted by a most unexpected noise, *Zzzzzz*. It sounded half like a steel giggle and half like a brass hiccough. It made the engine uneasy. He was sure someone was laughing at him. Proudly, he turned his large headlight till it lighted up a funny little automobile, which was laughing and shaking.

"You silly little road beetle," shouted the great engine. "What's wrong with you?"

The automobile gave one great shake and turned off his spark. He said in an orderly voice, "It struck my funny bone to hear you say you went everywhere on land, that's all. Don't you realize you're an old fuss-budget with your steam and your boiler and your fire and what not?

"You're tied to your rails! If everything
about your old tracks isn't kept just so, you
tumble into a ditch or do some fool thing.
Now I can stand real hardships. I use sparks
and gasoline! You just sit right there, you
rail-clinger, and watch me take that hill!"
Honk, honk, he was off up the hill.

The engine slowly turned his headlight till
the lights shone full on his shiny rails. He
thought, "He called me a rail-clinger—yes,
that I am. How can that crazy little beetle

run without tracks? I'm afraid he's much more wonderful than I!"

Now the automobile went jouncing and bouncing up the rough road. As he puffed merrily along he thought, "I'm mighty pleased with myself. Look at the way I climb this hill. There's nothing really so wonderful as I!"

Just then he heard a sound that made his engine boil with fright. *Dzdzdzdz*—it seemed to come right out of the sky. He got all his courage together and turned his searchlights up. The sight instantly killed his engine. Above him soared a giant airplane.

"*Dzdzdzdzdz*. You think you're so wonderful, you poor little creeping worm tied to earth," the airplane called. "I pity all of you slow things that I look down on as I fly through the high blue sky.

"Ox made way for horse, horse made way for engine, trolley car, and auto, but all—all made way for me! If you want speed, I'm what you need. Watch me."

The great airplane wheeled and rose like a great bird. The automobile watched him, too humbled to speak. Up, up, up went the plane— up, up, up till it was out of sight.

THE WORLD'S CHILDREN

BETJE'S TULIP

One spring morning in Holland the door of a gray stone farmhouse opened wide. Betje Van Royen stood in the doorway. She was dressed in a white starched cap, tight bodice, and full skirt above sock-covered feet.

Betje was carrying a small flowerpot that held a tiny yellow tulip. Happily, she stepped into the *klompen* (wooden shoes) lying side by side. Then she hurried down the path to Herr Van Royen, her father.

Today Betje was going with Father to the market square. She was taking her own little plant. Father had told her that when any of her flowers were ready, she could take them to the market with him and sell them.

For days Betje had weeded and watered her small garden. She had cared for each plant very tenderly. Then, yesterday, the time had come when the tulips seemed just right to be taken up and put into pots.

Father told her to pick out the tulips she wanted to take to market, but Betje's mind was already made up. She would take only one. This was her prize. It was the best of all

218

the tulips to come from the bulbs her Grannie
Van Royen had given her.

"You'll never have blossoms from these!"
a friend had said. "Who ever saw such tiny
bulbs? If they do bloom no one will notice
them, because they are so small. People
want big plants!"

Betje didn't let her friend's words bother
her. Deep down in her heart she was sure that
Grannie Van Royen knew all there was to
know about tulips. Why, Grannie's bulbs sold
all over the world!

As Betje came to the end of the path, she saw Father hitching Jan, the big brown dog, to the small flower cart. Near him, Tinker, the big black horse, was standing hitched to the large cart. Betje's eyes danced as she looked at the two carts filled with flowers.

"I've saved a place here for your tulip," Father said as he set Betje's plant between a big white tulip and a purple one.

Betje laughed. "I can hardly see it there. It is so little!"

Betje's laughter didn't last long. Her face clouded. Suppose her tulip was too small, after all. People might not even see it among all the big flowers.

"It's a beautiful tulip!" Father's voice was cheerful as he stopped to look at the tiny yellow flower. "Even though it is very small, it's as perfect as any I've seen."

Now Father started walking along the path beside Tinker. "You and Jan follow me," he told Betje. So Betje started walking along beside Jan. As she walked, the clump, clump of her wooden shoes kept time to the old Dutch lullaby she hummed softly to herself.

When they came near a bend in the canal, Betje's heart beat faster. She could see the market place! The tiled roofs of many red, gray, and white brick houses glistened in the bright morning sun.

Once they reached the square, Betje followed right behind Father until they came to his booth. Then he tied Jan and Tinker to a post. Betje helped him carry the plants to the table inside the booth.

"We'll put yours right here," Father said, and he made room for Betje's tiny yellow tulip

in the center of the front row. "Now no one can possibly miss seeing it."

When the table was all ready, Father said, "Betje, go and see the other booths before the crowd arrives. I'll take care of things here." He put a coin into Betje's hand. "You might like to stop at the *Wafelen Huis* (waffle house) for a cup of hot chocolate. Perhaps you can buy a little cake, too."

Betje smiled her thanks and walked to the front of the table. "I hope," she whispered to her tiny yellow flower, "if anyone buys you before I come back, he will love you just as much as I do."

Betje's eyes were like saucers as she went from one booth to another. There were booths with toys, dolls, picture books, needlework, pottery, jewelry, little cakes, and all kinds of candies. Other booths had piles of bright, round, red cheeses in them, or dried fish that dangled from poles.

There were more flower booths, too! Betje stopped to look at them. In not one did she find a tulip as tiny as hers! Father's plants, Betje thought, were more beautiful than any of the others at the market.

As Betje turned in at the *Wafelen Huis*, she stopped. Mother couldn't come today because she was finishing a new dress for Betje. Mother loved market days, and she liked those nice long chocolate bars for sale at the candy booth. The hot chocolate and the freshly-made, little cakes smelled good to Betje, too.

Betje looked at the coin in her hand, and her *klompen* clattered to the candy booth. Quickly, she bought a bar of chocolate and started off, but she turned at the sound of the candy lady's voice. "You've forgotten your change!" She handed Betje three small coins.

Betje's face brightened. She not only had a gift for her mother, but she had enough money left to buy at least a cup of chocolate. She hurried on to the *Wafelen Huis*.

"That's just enough for a cup of chocolate and a small cake," the man at the *Wafelen Huis* told Betje as he counted her coins.

While she sat there enjoying her tasty drink and sweet, a gay melody floated through the

room. The band was playing its first selection in the market square.

Suddenly the door of the *Wafelen Huis* flew open. Father stood in the doorway. "Betje, come quickly to the booth," he called.

Puzzled, Betje slid down from her chair and hurried after him. Had anything happened to her plant? Surely no one could have bought it! Father would have told her. Why, then, was he in such a rush?

Breathless, she stood before her father's booth. Father was busy talking to a strange man and woman. Where was her tiny yellow tulip? Betje searched the table.

"This is my little girl, Betje," Father said to the strangers.

Then he turned to her. "Betje, I want you to meet Mr. and Mrs. Anderson from America. Mr. Anderson was born in Amsterdam but now lives in the United States. He is a flower grower, too. And to think my Betje——"

"Think what?" Betje asked herself, becoming impatient as Father stooped to reach for her yellow tulip plant. It had been sitting behind a box in the back of the flower cart.

"Mr. Anderson wants to buy your plant.

225

He wants to take it back to America, and he wants all the others you have of this size, too. He grows and sells only miniature plants, tiny ones like yours!" Father's voice shook with excitement when he said all this.

"Wants—to buy—my yellow tulip—my plants—all of them?" Betje stammered.

"That I do!" said Mr. Anderson. "I've never seen a tulip like yours. It's a little beauty. Why, it's perfect!"

"Have you named it?" Mrs. Anderson asked, smiling at Betje kindly.

Before Betje could answer the question, she heard Mr. Anderson saying, "I have it! Let's call it *Betje's Tulip!*"

"Good! Good!" Father smiled his approval.

"Now," Mr. Anderson said as he took the tiny plant from Father and gave it to Betje, "will you please stand in front of the booth, Betje? I want to take a picture of the plant and its grower. It will be finished in color."

"Hold the plant closer to you," said Mrs. Anderson. "That's it."

Betje smiled and then she heard a click. She was going to the United States with her tiny yellow tulip!

226

GOLDEN AMAK

Young Lee Spencer never forgot his first sight of Amak. It happened one day while Lee, on snowshoes, was taking some medicine to the old sourdough on Indian Creek. A sudden movement on a snowy ridge caught his attention, and he looked up straight into the eyes of a great golden Husky.

Amak was the largest, most beautiful dog the boy ever had seen. He looked so wild and proud against the blue Alaskan sky. For one breathless moment, boy and beast stared at each other. Then the Husky was gone.

"I must hurry with Mr. Beck's medicine," Lee told himself. "I can't go chasing around after wild dogs."

"If my back wasn't so stiff, I'd come to the village for the medicine myself," the old prospector said when Lee reached the cabin. "You're Dr. Spencer's son, aren't you?"

"Yes, sir," answered the boy. Lee had great respect for the gray-bearded sourdough. Mr. Beck had one of the finest dog teams south of the Yukon, and also was said to be a good dog doctor. "Mr. Beck," Lee said, "I just saw the wild dog, Amak!"

The sourdough scowled. "He's really a bad one, that dog!"

"Is he part wolf?" Lee asked. "Does he lead a wolf pack, as people say?"

"Sometimes he runs with wolves," said the old sourdough. "He and the pack will make trouble this winter, the same as last year, unless the hunters get them."

"I hope no one ever catches Amak," Lee said. "He's such a beauty!"

The old man looked at the boy sharply. "You like dogs, don't you?"

"Oh, yes, sir!" was the reply.

228

The old man seemed pleased. "Well, then," he said, "maybe you'd like to help train some pups. I can't train them with a bad back."

"I'd like that very much!" cried Lee.

Training the pups was fun, Lee discovered. He learned much about dogs as the weeks passed. Still, he often thought of the golden Amak, wild and free, in the lonely hills.

Lee was on a walk through the hills when he saw Amak again. He heard the sound first, a thin whine in the distance. Then he saw Amak lying in the snow, thin and half-starved. The dog tried to rise when Lee approached, but his strength was gone. He could only bare his fangs in an angry snarl.

"You've broken a leg, Amak!" Lee cried in

alarm. "Some big deer must have kicked you!" Trembling with excitement, Lee drew a sandwich from his pocket, unwrapped it, and tossed it to the big dog.

Amak wolfed it up in a second, and his brown eyes begged for more.

"That's all I have," Lee said, sitting down on the ground a few feet away. "I'm going to stay here for a while and talk to you. Mr. Beck says that dogs understand more than most people think they do."

The dog rested his head on his paws, but his wary eyes never left the boy. He seemed suspicious, puzzled. Perhaps he remembered a cruel master who had caused him to run away and hate all human beings.

Slowly the boy moved closer, talking softly all the while. Finally he held out his hand, palm up, as Mr. Beck had taught him.

Without warning the big dog lunged, slashing out with fangs that missed Lee's outstretched hand only by inches.

The boy jerked back, shivering with fright, but finally he smiled. "I don't blame you, Amak. It was my fault. I must make you like and trust me before I pet you."

Suddenly he knew what he had to do. Amak must be saved, and the old sourdough was the person who could do it. Lee ran all the way to Mr. Beck's cabin.

The old man listened and shook his head. "Not much you can do with a dog that has gone wild," he explained soberly. He took down his rifle. "A critter like that with a broken leg is much better off dead."

Lee caught his breath. "Please, Mr. Beck!" he begged. "I want to take care of him."

The old man hesitated. "You think a lot of that dog, don't you, Lee?"

Lee could only nod his head.

"Well," said the sourdough, "we can try to save him, but if he can't be trained there's only one thing to do."

Mr. Beck harnessed his dog team, and he and Lee drove back to Amak. Mr. Beck worked capsules into a frozen salmon and tossed the fish to the dog. "That will put him to sleep so we can set his broken leg," he said.

When Amak awakened, he was tied up in one of Mr. Beck's dog stalls, and his leg was held tightly in splints.

Then his training began. For an hour each day, Lee sat with him, talking and sometimes singing. "I want you to get used to me," he told the golden Husky. "Then Mr. Beck will have a wonderful new dog. You won't have any more trouble with hunters, and I can come to see you whenever I like."

Amak whined.

"I know your leg hurts, but we'll soon take off those splints. Then you'll feel fine."

The days flew by and Amak began to regain his strength. He no longer flattened his ears when Lee came close. His golden fur began to shine again. Lee felt sure that Amak would be one of the best lead dogs in Alaska.

232

One day Lee took a stick and shoved one end of it into the stall, teasing Amak as if he were a kitten. With a yip, Amak grabbed at the stick playfully.

Lee smiled. Now he knew the dog liked him. He walked boldly into the stall, cleaned it, and spread new straw while Amak sniffed at his heels excitedly.

Lee let his fingers rest on the glossy coat of the big Husky. The dog stiffened and began to tremble. His ears were flat again.

The boy held his breath. He stroked the dog's back gently. Talking in low tones all

the time, he worked his fingers up into the thick fur on Amak's neck.

"Just wait," he whispered. "There, you see? I'm rubbing behind your ears now. That's where a dog likes to be rubbed!"

He kept stroking and talking until Amak's ears came up. The two were really friends now, and Lee was so filled with happiness that his eyes smarted with tears.

Three days later Amak allowed the boy to cut off the splints. Mr. Beck said proudly, "The leg is perfect! Now he needs exercise. You've done well with him, Lee!"

So, with Amak on a strong chain leash, Lee took him for long walks in the hills every day. They raced, played games, and tumbled together in the snow. Their friendship became a beautiful and shining thing.

The people of the village were startled one day when the sourdough and Lee came walking down the street. They had Amak on a leash and went to Dr. Spencer's office. Lee was startled, too, because Mr. Beck hadn't mentioned seeing Dr. Spencer.

"This is Amak, Dr. Spencer," explained Mr. Beck. "There are few boys in the country who would have had patience enough to train this dog. Don't you think your son has earned the right to keep him?"

Lee glanced anxiously at his father. Then he saw the proud look that spread over the doctor's face.

"Yes, I think he has! My son has proved he is wise enough to have a dog of his own."

Lee was filled with happiness. He gave Amak a big hug, and Amak licked his face.

As soon as Lee could speak, he turned to his father. "Amak's going to be at the head of your dog team some day," he said. "He'll be the best lead dog south of the Yukon."

FREIGHT BOATS

Boats that carry sugar
And tobacco from Havana;
Boats that carry coconuts
And coffee from Brazil;
Boats that carry cotton
From the city of Savannah;
Boats that carry anything
From any place you will!

Boats like boxes loaded down
With tons of sand and gravel;
Boats with blocks of granite
For a building on the hill;
Boats that measure many thousand
Lonesome miles of travel
As they carry anything
From any place you will!

From *I Go A-Traveling* by James S. Tippett. Copyright, 1929,
Harper & Brothers. Copyright, 1957, James S. Tippett.

236

MONSIEUR CLOP-CLOP

A year ago Pierre Repos, eight years old, had come to the city of Quebec from a farm on the French-Canadian island of Orleans. Pierre had never spoken a word of English, but he could read it a little, and understood it quite well in school. His papa and mama could neither speak, read, nor understand it.

On the island, where everyone said *"Bon jour,"* there was no need to say "Good morning." However, it was quite different in the city of Quebec.

Because he could not speak English, the only work that Pierre's papa could find was washing dishes all day long in a big hotel. This was dull, indoor work.

Pierre was lonely. He missed the horses on the farm. One day he walked to work with Papa, since he had nothing else to do.

As he started home again, Pierre heard a familiar *clop, clop, clippety clop.* There, crossing the square, was a beautiful dappled gray horse. The fine horse was drawing a bouncing, two-wheeled carriage.

The carriage stopped near Pierre. When

the driver had finished talking, the passengers handed him some money to pay for the sight-seeing trip they'd just taken.

"Now that is work my papa would like," said Pierre to himself, "but he cannot speak English. He doesn't think he can learn."

What a beautiful, beautiful horse! Pierre stroked the velvety, gray-and-white coat. The horse whinnied and snuffled. Pierre clapped his hands, and the carriage driver smiled a big Irish smile.

"You like the horse, lad?" he asked.

"Oh, yes, sir," said Pierre, forgetting all about being afraid of trying to speak English. "I think he likes me, too."

"Sure, and he does, lad. A horse always knows a friend."

"I have *un ami,* a friend!" cried Pierre.

"Come to see us often, lad," said the Irishman heartily. "My name is Jerry, and the horse's name is——"

"I know," shouted Pierre. "His name is Monsieur Clop-Clop."

"Have it your own way, lad," said the driver with a laugh.

Every day after that Pierre went to talk to his friend Monsieur Clop-Clop, and to Jerry, for Jerry was very friendly.

Pierre learned that Jerry lived alone and that he wanted to go back to Ireland. He also learned that Jerry didn't like his own cooking and never had a decent meal.

It was then that Pierre got his idea.

He invited Jerry home to dinner. After the driver had eaten all of Mama's fine French pancakes, Pierre jumped up. "Tell us what you say to the people you take around the city," Pierre begged. "Please say it in English. We must learn that language."

So Jerry gave his speech, just as though people were riding behind him in the carriage. Then Papa tried to say it after him.

Every time Jerry came to dinner after that, and he came quite often, he gave the speech again. He repeated over and over what he said to the people he took through the city. Each time Jerry did this, Pierre would ask his papa to repeat all of it, in English.

Papa did better and better as time went on. Soon he was trying other English words and phrases, and Mama joined the game, too.

One day Pierre said to Papa, "Why not ask the man who owns the carriages if you may drive one of them? Show him how well you can tell about interesting places."

How Papa laughed! "Aha, now I see what your plan is, my little one!"

That day Pierre could hardly wait until his papa came home. He went to the square to tell Monsieur Clop-Clop what was happening. The horse nodded his head up and down, as if he understood.

Alas, Papa didn't get to drive one of the

horses. The owner said that all the carriages had drivers. He did take Papa's name, though, and said he would let him know.

Pierre and Papa were very sad.

A month later something even worse happened. When Pierre went to the square to take a carrot to Monsieur Clop-Clop, there was no gray-and-white horse! No *clop, cloppety-clop*. No Jerry. Where could they be? Had Pierre lost his two good friends?

When he got back home he heard voices. In the living room sat Jerry and Papa talking. They were speaking in English!

"The horse," asked Pierre, "where is he?"

"In the stable where he belongs," replied Jerry, winking at Papa.

"I waited for you all day," said Pierre.

"Did you now?" asked Jerry, "and me at home, getting ready for my journey back to the fair land of Ireland."

"To *Ireland?* What about Monsieur Clop-Clop? What about him?" asked Pierre.

"Oh, him," said Jerry. "Sure, he has a new master now, a fine young man who will treat him very well."

Pierre had tears in his eyes, but he was glad to know of Monsieur Clop-Clop's good fortune. Perhaps he might still be able to see the horse once in a while.

In the morning Papa asked, "Would you like to walk to work with me today?"

Pierre ran to get his béret. Now he'd see Monsieur Clop-Clop again, and perhaps he'd get to meet the new driver.

When they reached the square Papa said, "We must find the horse for you before I go on to my work."

Pierre looked up and down the street.

There he was, Monsieur Clop-Clop, at the

end of the line. Head up, he was jerking at the rein held by the stable boy.

"But where is the driver, the fine young man?" asked Pierre.

"*C'est moi!* It is I!" shouted Papa, thumping his chest. "I am the fine young man! No more dishes to wash! From now on, I drive the horse through this beautiful city!"

"Monsieur Clop-Clop!" shouted Pierre, jumping about on one leg. "Did you hear that? Now I will get to ride with you. It is a fine language, this English—a very fine language. Papa will tell you!"

AMIGO, MY BURRO

He is my friend—my little burro! It is for this reason I have named him "Amigo." I am very lucky to have such a fine friend, as you will know when you hear my story.

There are many little ones in my family. I am the eldest son. One month ago, on my tenth birthday, my uncle gave me a small, gentle gray burro.

My burro and I were together almost all the time. While he nibbled grasses that grew near our tiny adobe house, I did my work. After I split the wood, carried the water, and fed grain to our faithful hens, I ran eagerly to the place where my burro was feeding.

In the mornings I pleased my small sisters by putting them upon my burro's back. He carried them around in circles for a while. When he tired of this, he would lie down and refuse to move, even for me, his master.

When the midafternoon sun grew warm, my sisters were called in for their *siesta*. Then my small burro and I would ride forth to explore, and to be admired by my very good friends in the village near by.

Life is pleasant in the summertime for children of Mexico. They can then enjoy warm weather and beautiful blue skies. It is even more pleasant when a boy has his own burro that he can ride over many peaceful trails. Never was life so good, I thought.

One day, however, my beautiful world was turned upside down and went whirling around me. My mother told me that the little burro must be sold.

I could not speak. I must not weep, for ever since my tenth birthday I had been called "Manuel." That meant that I had grown up. I was no longer "Manuelito," which meant "Little Manuel," who had not grown up.

Even as Manuelito, I never had wept much.

Now I could not think of it. So I remained silent until I was able to ask my mother why this terrible thing must be done.

Her eyes were kind as she told me that we were poorer than usual. She said there would always be beans bubbling in the pot for her children, but school would be starting soon in the village. There were no proper clothes for me or for my sisters.

I looked down at my clothes. What did they matter? What difference did it make if I wore clothes that had been many times mended? I would not care so long as I rode to school on my beautiful little gray burro.

My mother understood how I felt. Still, we both knew that Maria and Teresa must have good clothes, even if I could get along with what I had. My mother was not able to think of any words to comfort me. I hugged her and told her not to worry—that everything would be all right. Already I had a plan.

Without saying more, I ran outside to my burro, who seemed to be wondering why I had not come sooner. He nudged me with his soft black nose. I put my arms about his neck and hugged him. I whispered into one of his long shaggy ears that he must not worry—everything was going to be all right.

My plan was that I would make the burro so useful to us that we could not afford to be without him. Into the hills we would go, my burro and I, and bring back bundles of wood to sell in the village. With the money I would earn, my mother could buy dresses for my little sisters.

I called to my mother that I would take a ride on my burro and might be gone till after sundown. This was not unusual, as I did the same thing nearly every afternoon.

247

Then I rode straight for the low hills. Even the burro seemed to feel my excitement, for he turned his slow walk to a trot.

"This is Wednesday," I thought to myself as we jogged along. "Friday is Market Day in the village. I must have a good-sized load of wood to sell on that day."

When we reached the spot where I would gather the wood, I slid from my burro's back. The wood was mostly loose branches I found lying around under bushes. It was just right for tying into bundles to be carried on the back of a small gray burro.

I gathered one nice pile of wood and began to look around for more. A stick lay under the bush before me. It would be a good one for my next bundle. As I leaned down to pick it up, a terrible warning buzzed through the clear summer air.

A rattlesnake!

I had stepped over the snake as I leaned down to pick up the stick. Now he was in front of me, coiled and ready to strike. I looked about, wondering what to do.

My burro heard the rattle. He seemed to know that he must protect me. Before the

snake could strike, the burro had stamped on him with his sharp little front hoofs.

Although now I was Manuel, too big a boy to cry, I did cry—burying my head in the shaggy little burro's neck.

"Gracias, amigo! Gracias! Thank you, friend! Thank you!" I said over and over.

Now you can see how I came to name my burro Amigo. He is truly my friend.

On Market Day, Amigo and I were among the first to arrive at the market place. We picked out a spot where all would be sure to see the fine load of wood I had brought from the hills. "Soon the customers will come and buy!" I told myself and my burro.

The warm noon sun beat down. Still, I had sold only a very small amount of wood.

I watched the stall next to mine as eagerly as I did my own. This was because its owner was selling his goods fast. It was also because I was wishing with all my heart that I, too, could be buying his goods. The man was selling cloth—all kinds of cloth.

The day passed, but try as I might, I had earned only a few coins. This would not be enough to buy clothing for my sisters. It would not save my little gray burro!

The sun disappeared over the hills, and the people began to pack up their wares to go home. They would not be back for a week, and that might be too late!

The man next to me was also getting ready to go. He had sold most of his cloth. Only small pieces of bright calico and a few bits of dark-colored wool remained.

Then a thought struck me. Perhaps I could make a trade with him. He might be willing to let me have the cloth that remained, if I would deliver to his home all the wood I had

left. The cloth was not as pretty as I had hoped to get, but it was better than nothing. Fearfully, I stepped up to the man and told him what I had in mind.

For a few moments he was silent. I was very much afraid I'd made him angry. Then he placed his hand on my shoulder.

"My son," he said, "you are welcome to take the cloth. I only fear that it will not be a really fair trade."

Quickly, I told him that I would be more than glad to bring him another load of wood if this one was not enough.

"Why, my son, are you so eager to sell your fine wood for these few remaining bits of my cloth?" he asked kindly.

I told him about Amigo, my burro, and the danger of losing him.

"This small amount of cloth will not be of much use to you, I fear," said the man, looking very thoughtful.

In alarm, I quickly told him I would try very hard to gather more wood for him before it was too late.

"Your mother can be well-pleased with you," the man said. "Tell her that if you are allowed to keep your little burro, she will not need to worry about warm clothes for your sisters or for yourself. In exchange for more wood, I will promise to give you plenty of cloth for all of you."

Once again, I, Manuel with the grown-up name, nearly wept. This time I wept for joy. In spite of my feeling, I was soon able to thank the man for his great kindness.

In the coming twilight, my friend, Amigo, and I started for home. I was sure that if he could have known what had happened, his heart would have been as happy as mine.

THE DRAGON CHAIR

Olaf Glunt was sitting by the fire, reading. As usual, he was sitting in the dragon chair— the "kubbe stool," as it was called in Norway.

Neither of the girls who were knitting by the fire ever sat in the dragon chair. It was not because they were afraid of the dragon. It was because they felt the chair was too lovely to be sat in by anyone but their father, who had spent seven years carving it.

The carving was so beautiful that Guri often sat and gazed at it. No matter how often she followed the scroll around the chair, it always turned out that the dragon had his tail in his mouth.

Tonight Guri was knitting a pair of red socks and her sister was knitting a pair, too. Guri had knit socks before, but her sister was knitting her first pair.

"Who is going to buy your socks when you have finished them?" Liza Beth asked.

Guri knit another round before she answered, "They are for Hans."

"For him?" echoed her sister. "He can never afford to buy them."

"He isn't going to buy them," said Guri.

"You aren't going to give them to him, are you?" asked her sister.

"Yes, I am," said Guri. "Since his mother died there's no one to knit new socks for him or even mend his old ones."

"Why doesn't he mend them himself?"

"Boys don't know how to mend socks," Guri declared. "That's girls' work."

"Pooh! Hans doesn't know how to do boys' work, either. He can only whittle and carve things out of wood!"

"Well, you can't do that, can you?" cried Guri. "So maybe he's as smart as you are— maybe even smarter!"

"I thought you said you were going to save

254

your knitting money and buy yourself a kubbe stool," Liza Beth went on.

"I am."

"You'll never have one if you give away everything you knit," warned Liza Beth.

"Just the same," said Guri, "I'm going to give these socks to Hans tomorrow. Tomorrow is his birthday."

"I think you are foolish," said her sister. "Why don't you give to those who can give something in return?"

"Never you mind," said Guri. "You sell your socks and save your coins, but you'll see! I'll have a chair as soon as you!"

Guri knitted away as fast as she could, but she couldn't help glancing over at her father, sitting in his dragon chair. She and Liza Beth had only footstools to sit on, just as if they were small children. They wanted to call themselves big, but they could not until they had chairs of their own.

"When I finish this pair, I am going to make a pair for Thorvald. He will need them when he goes to the winter fishing," said Guri.

"Are you going to give them away, too?" Liza Beth asked her sister.

"What are you talking about?" demanded the mother, getting up from her spinning wheel and coming over to the girls.

"Mother, Guri is going to give that pair of socks to Gul Par's Hans," said Liza Beth.

"Well," said the mother, "the wool belongs to Guri, so if she wants to give the socks away, why shouldn't she?"

Just then the father folded his paper and put it down on the table. "It is time to go to bed," he said, and the mother thought so, too. Guri had hoped they would stay up for a while longer, because she wanted to finish the sock before bedtime.

She did not beg to stay up, but she watched her father. When he went to the corner by the door and pulled his boots off by using the shoe iron, she knew he meant what he said.

Without waiting to be told, Guri put her knitting away. The sock was not finished, and Guri was sorry about that. She would have to finish it the next day.

Tomorrow would be Guri's birthday, too, but she had not thought much about it. In Norway, a person's "name day"—that is, the day on which he was named—is much more important than a birthday.

Hans probably felt the same way. Still, it would be nice if she could finish the socks and give them to him on his birthday.

Guri awoke the next morning as soon as she heard her mother putting the kettle on the fire. She dressed quickly, and by the time the coffee was ready, she had knit two more rounds on the red sock.

When it was time to leave for school, all Guri had left to do was gather the sock at the toe. It wouldn't take more than half an hour to finish the sock now.

Guri saw Hans at school that day. She saw a hole in his sock, too. For once, she was almost glad the hole was there. Think, just think, how good Hans would feel when he had a new pair of socks! She chuckled when she thought what fun it would be to surprise him with the present she had made.

"It is your birthday," said Hans, when he and Guri met in the hall. "Luck, good health, and many years of happiness, I wish you."

"The same I wish you," said Guri and went on into the schoolroom. Her eyes were twinkling. She was thinking how happy Hans would be when he saw the red socks.

Guri was eager to go home and finish the sock. She thought the day would never end. Hans thought the day was long, too, but not for the same reason.

Finally school was dismissed. Hans shot out of the schoolroom and jumped on his skis. Off he raced across the snowdrifts.

"Hurry, Liza Beth!" said Guri, standing on her own skis, "or I won't wait for you."

"Don't wait," said Liza Beth. "I am going to set the cupboard to rights for the school-master before I go home."

Guri didn't wait to say any more to her sister. She set off over the fjord, with her skis swishing through the snow.

Her mother and father were having coffee when she came in, but she had no time to join them. She sat down on her stool and took up the red sock again.

"Aren't you going to have a bite to eat?" asked the mother, in surprise.

"No. Today is Hans's birthday and I want to finish the sock so I can take the pair over tonight before it is too dark."

Hans lived in a little hut set well back in the woods. It was never very light there in the wintertime.

At last the sock was finished. "May I go now?" Guri asked her mother. She hardly waited for the reply before she was on her skis with the socks in her pocket.

Guri stood on her skis, braced herself, bent forward a little, and took off. How the wind sang in her ears! Skiing was fun!

In a little while she reached the hut in the woods. She knew a warm blaze was burning inside, for the windows gleamed. Hans was at home. She set her skis up in the snow and rapped on the door.

"Come in," said a voice.

Guri entered. Hans was sitting on the floor

in front of the fire. He was holding a narrow knife, hooked at the end like a button hook. Guri knew it well. It was the carving knife he was always using. He had been carving something out of wood again.

When Hans saw Guri, he sprang up.

"Oh, it is you!" he said, as though he could scarcely believe his eyes.

"Yes," said Guri. "I have made a pair of socks for your birthday." So saying, she took the socks out of her pocket.

Hans took the socks in his hands. He didn't say thank you. It had been so long since any-one had given him anything that he had for-

gotten what to say! Guri, however, didn't notice that. She had walked over to the fire to see what Hans was carving now.

"Why, it's a kubbe stool!" she cried in surprise. "It's lovely! Surely you didn't make it all by yourself?"

"Oh, yes," said Hans, as if that was not much of anything. "I even cut down a tree to get the wood for it."

Guri stooped to see whether there was a dragon with a long winding tail on this kubbe stool, as there was on her father's.

"Why," she cried in amazement, " 'Guri'

has been carved on it. How did it get there?"
She traced the name with her finger.

"I put it there," said Hans, taking up the
crooked carving knife to dot the *i*. "You see,
I am making this kubbe stool for you. It is
for your birthday."

Guri was too surprised to speak.

Later in the evening, Liza Beth looked out
of the window. "Guri is coming home now,"
she said to her mother. "Hans is with her.
He has his sled, and I believe they are bringing home a block of wood."

Liza Beth took up her sock and sat down by
the fire. "I suppose Guri found a chunk of
wood that had fallen off somebody's wood
load," she added, and began to knit very fast.

Hans helped Guri with the kubbe stool,
but he wouldn't come inside.

Guri rushed into the house. "Mother,
come and see what Hans has made for me!"
she cried.

The chair was brought in and placed by the
fireplace. Guri sat down in it and stretched
her feet out in front of her. Liza Beth didn't
say a thing. She was still working away on
her first pair of socks.

RING AROUND THE WORLD

Ring around the world
Taking hands together,
All across the temperate
And the torrid weather.
Past the royal palm-trees,
By the ocean sand,
Make a ring around the world,
Taking each other's hand;
In the valleys, on the hill,
Over the prairie spaces,
There's a ring around the world
Made of children's friendly faces.

From *All Through the Year* by Annette Wynne. Copyright, 1932, 1959, by Annette Wynne. Published by J. B. Lippincott Company.

STORYLAND TRAILS

OUT OF THE WORLD

There was once an unhappy boy who thought this world was not a very nice place.

The thing he most disliked about the world was that it was so stupidly regular. You always knew when the sun would rise and when it would set. You knew that when the sun set—and sometimes even sooner—your mother would come and tell you it was time to eat your supper and get ready for bed.

It was just the same about getting up. Everything went round and round in the same way. You could hardly ever do what you wanted to, because it was always time for you to do something else.

There were other bad things about the world, too. You had to wait and wait, and this made you impatient. If you wanted Christmas to come in November, there was no way to manage it. It was hardest of all to have to wait to be ten years old.

The boy's father had told him of a good many fine things he could do when he was ten years old. Well, nothing was ever so slow in coming as that tenth birthday! The nearer it came—according to the calendar—the slower and slower it was about it.

A week before the birthday was to be there, the boy asked his father if he would please hurry it up in some way. If he could not do that, would he please buy him another that could be delivered at once?

The father shook his head and showed the boy the calendar. He told him that birthdays could not be hurried—that they really came more slowly if you tried to hurry them.

At last, three nights before his birthday was really to come, the boy made up his mind he could stand it no longer. Jumping out of bed, he stood by the window and looked up at the stars. They were shining so brightly

it seemed as if you could reach out and touch each one of them.

The boy remembered that each star was a world in itself. He made up his mind that if he could only get to one, he would live there much more happily than on the earth.

He had never thought before that it might be possible to do this. However, he believed his father might help him. His father was very wise, and knew many things he never told. His father studied the stars, and he might know how to get to them.

So the boy went very quietly through the hall and knocked at the door of his father's room. His father said, "Come in."

"I want to see you about something very important," said the boy. "I'm so tired of this world I've decided to go to some other world, if I possibly can. I thought perhaps you could show me how to get to a star."

His father didn't say anything for a long time. Then he said, "I suppose I could let you have my Light Magnet."

"What is that?" asked the boy.

"It is a very strong magnet that works with light. If you hold it where a lamp can shine on it, you will be drawn across the room to the light. You'll be drawn so gently you'll hardly know what has happened. The magnet could draw you all the way to a star."

"That would be fine!" cried the boy, clapping his hands.

When his father was sure the boy really intended to go, he went to his desk and took out the Light Magnet. It looked very much like a round stone. In the center of it was a spot like a mirror, which reflected any light that shone on it.

The boy took the wonderful thing and went back to his room. He put on his overcoat so that he would not be cold while traveling.

Then he opened the window and sat down on the ledge with his feet hanging outside.

Turning the magnet straight toward the star that seemed nearest and brightest, the boy waited to see what would happen. At first, nothing did. The boy was afraid his father was wrong in thinking the magnet would work with a light so far away.

In another minute, he felt the magnet give a little tug in his hands. When he held it tightly, it pulled at his arms and then at his whole body. Before he really knew what was happening, he had been drawn off the window ledge and was moving through the air like a great bird.

He was almost frightened when he looked down and saw the lights of his father's house grow dimmer beneath him. Then he looked up and saw the star seem to come nearer, and he was glad he was leaving the earth. "Hurrah!" he shouted, as he moved swiftly along.

Of course, he had no way to measure time, so he couldn't tell how long a journey he was taking. Soon, however, the star stopped looking like a big light. Instead, it looked like a world! The sun was shining on it, and there were hills, and valleys, and cities, as there were on the earth he had left behind.

Then in a few minutes more the boy landed on the ground. "Hurrah!" he cried again. "Now I am in another world."

He walked some distance before he met anyone, for he had landed in open country. At last he saw a man walking toward him.

"You seem to be a stranger," said the man.

"Yes," said the boy, "I've just come from the world and landed on your star. Did you ever meet anyone from the world?"

"Why, this is the world," said the man. "I guess you must mean that you have come from one of the stars."

The boy didn't want to be rude, so he said, "Well, I suppose it all depends on how you look at it."

"Why did you come away from your star?"

"Oh, I didn't like it at all," said the boy. "For one thing, the sun rises and sets every day at about the same time. You have to go to bed when it sets and get up when it rises. I decided I should like to go to a world where the sun shines all the time. I'm glad to find it shining here, although it is night."

"But it isn't night at all," said the man. "It's the middle of the day with us. After a while the sun will set, just as it does in your own world."

"I'm sorry to hear that!" said the boy. "I had no idea it would be so in any world but mine. Of course, there were other reasons for not liking my world. Each year was very long. You couldn't have a Christmas or a birthday until the day came."

"How long was a year?" asked the man.

"Three hundred and sixty-five days," said the boy. "Don't you think that's a pretty long time for a year?"

"Well, I don't know," said the man. "Our years are always four hundred and seventy days long. No longer, no shorter."

"My goodness! Do you have only one birthday in a year?"

"Of course! How could we have more?"

"I don't know. I thought perhaps up here you could have a birthday any time."

"Why, we go around the sun just the way you do, and that is what makes years," said the man.

"And do you have to wait a long time for winter when you want snow, and another long time for summer when you want green

grass and flowers? I thought perhaps up here you could have summer one day and winter the next, if you happened to want it so."

"I don't know where you'd find a world like that," the man said, shaking his head.

The boy was almost ready to cry, but he would not do so before the man. "I think I'll go back to my own world," he said. "It seems as good as any. Will you show me where it is so that I shall not go to the wrong one?"

"Yes," said the man, "I can show you the way to your world tonight."

The moment it grew dark enough to see the stars come out, the man pointed to one of them. He told the boy that the star was really his own world. After thanking the man for his kindness, the boy turned his magnet toward the star. Soon, he was flying home.

As he went along, he thought how nice it was that his world *did* go about so regularly. Otherwise, he could never have been told where to find it. He might have had to wander from star to star all of his life.

When he walked into his own house again, his father came to meet him. "So you've come back," he said, with a smile.

"Yes," said the boy. "Your magnet is a very nice thing, but I've decided I like this world well enough, after all."

"Fine," said his father, "and it is good that you returned when you did. Your birthday supper is all ready. Everybody thought you'd surely come home in time for that. You know, your birthday will be over at twelve o'clock tonight. If you hadn't come back before then, I don't see that you would ever have become ten years old."

"How strange!" said the boy. "I never thought of that." Just then he smelled the birthday dinner and hurried off to eat it.

THE GLASS HILL

Once there was a man who had a meadow. In the meadow was a barn for hay, but there had been no hay in the barn for some time. Every year on St. John's night, when the meadow grass was thick and green, something came and ate it down to the ground.

The man finally tired of losing the grass that he wanted to cut and make into hay. Then he called his three sons to him.

"One of you must sleep in the barn on St. John's night," he said. "You must not let the grass be eaten again this year."

When evening came, the oldest son went to the barn and lay down to sleep. In the night

276

there came such a clatter that the walls and the roof shook and groaned. The lad jumped up and ran away as fast as he could without once looking back.

As for the grass, it was eaten up again, and there was no hay to put in the barn.

The next St. John's night the man sent his second oldest son to the barn. Like his older brother, he ran away as fast as he could when he heard a terrible noise. Again the grass was eaten to the ground.

The next St. John's night it was the youngest son's turn to watch. This lad was called Boots, because he did all the dirty work on the farm. When he made ready to go to the barn, his older brothers laughed at him.

"You're just the man to watch the grass," they said. "You've done nothing but sit in the cinders all your life!"

Boots didn't care what his brothers said. He went off to the barn and sat down. In the night, the barn began to creak and groan.

"Well," thought Boots, "if nothing worse than this happens, I can stand it."

Then came a great rumbling. It seemed as if the walls and roof were falling down. Boots sat still, and at last the rumbling stopped. Everything was still.

Soon, though, Boots heard a crunching noise outside the barn door. He peeked out. There stood a big fat horse, feeding away on the meadow grass. Such a fine horse Boots never had seen before. Its saddle and bridle were of gold. A full suit of armor lay on top of the saddle, and this, too, was of gold.

"Ho ho!" said Boots. "It's you who eats our grass. I'll stop that!"

He took the steel that he used for starting fires out of his tinder box and threw it over the horse. At once the beast became so tame that Boots could do whatever he wanted to do with it. He rode off on the horse and tied it in a secret hiding place.

When Boots arrived home on foot, his brothers asked how things had gone.

"Well," said Boots, "all I can say is that I sat in the barn till the sun rose."

"A pretty story," said the brothers, "but we'll soon see." Off they went to the meadow and found the grass standing as deep and thick as it had been the night before.

Now you must know that the king of the

country had a very beautiful daughter. He
wanted to find the finest and bravest man
that he could to marry his daughter.

You must also know that beside the palace
there was a high, high hill, all of glass. The
king decided that his daughter should sit at
the top of the glass hill, with a golden apple
in her lap. The man who could ride up the
hill and get the golden apple was to have the
princess for a wife. Morever, he was to have
half the kingdom, too.

The princess was so lovely that all who saw
her loved her. All the knights in the land
were eager to win her—and half the kingdom
besides. Knights came riding on high-pranc-
ing horses from all parts of the world. Each

one had made up his mind that he, and he alone, would carry off the golden apple.

At last the day of the trial came. Everyone in the country gathered at the glass hill. Everyone was eager to see the man who would win the princess for his wife.

The two elder brothers set off on their horses, but they wouldn't let Boots go with them. They feared people would laugh at them if they were seen with such a dirty, ragged fellow as he.

"Very well," said Boots, "it's all one to me. I shall go alone."

Now when the two brothers came to the glass hill, the knights were already trying to ride their horses up the hill. It was no use, though. As soon as the horses set foot on the hill, down they slipped.

Not one horse could ride up the hill, and no wonder! The hill was as slippery as ice, and as steep as a wall.

The knights wanted the princess and half the kingdom, so they kept on trying. They rode and slipped, and slipped and rode, and rode and slipped again.

The king was just thinking of calling off

the trial when a handsome knight came riding up on a fine horse. No one ever had seen the likes of horse or rider. He wore a suit of golden armor, and his horse had a golden saddle and bridle.

The princess, sitting on the top of the hill, thought, "Oh, I wish *he* would ride to the top and get the golden apple!"

This knight rode up the hill as if it were no trouble at all. At the top, he took the golden apple from the lap of the princess. Then he rode down again. Before anyone could stop him, he rode away.

On the next day all the knights passed before the king so that the one who had the golden apple might show it. Not one of them had it, of course.

"Well," said the king, "someone must have the apple. With our own eyes we saw a knight ride up the hill and carry it away."

So he ordered everyone in the kingdom to come before him. Boots's brothers were the last to come. The king asked them whether they knew any man who had not come.

"Well," said they, "we have a brother, but he's a dirty, ragged fellow who works in the cinders all day."

"Never mind that," said the king. "He must come before me, too."

When Boots came, the king said, "How now, have you the golden apple?"

"Yes, I have," said Boots. With that, he pulled the apple out of his pocket. At the same time, his dirty ragged clothes changed to a suit of shining golden armor.

"You," said the king, "shall have my daughter and half my kingdom."

After that, there was a great feast and much merry-making for all the people in the kingdom. And if they have not yet left off merry-making, they must still be at it.

A TRAGIC TALE

There lived a sage in days of yore,
And he a handsome pigtail wore;
But wondered much and sorrowed more
Because it hung behind him.

He mused upon this curious case,
And swore he'd change the pigtail's place,
And have it hanging at his face,
Not dangling there behind him.

Said he, "The mystery I've found—
I'll turn me round."
He turned him round,
But still it hung behind him.

Then round and round, and out and in,
All day the puzzled sage did spin;
In vain—it mattered not a pin—
The pigtail hung behind him.

And though his efforts never slack,
And though he twist and twirl and tack,
Alas! Still faithful to his back,
The pigtail hangs behind him!

HEIDI'S FIRST ADVENTURE

Morning sunlight flooded the room and Heidi awoke with a start. For a moment she couldn't imagine where she was. Then she heard a deep voice outside, and she remembered. Only yesterday, she had come to live on the mountain with her grandfather.

Heidi jumped out of bed and quickly put on her clothes. Then she climbed down the ladder and ran outside the hut. There stood Peter with the flock of goats. Grandfather was just bringing his two goats out of the shed to join the others. Heidi ran forward to wish him and the goats good morning.

"Do you want to go with them up the mountain?" asked Grandfather. Heidi fairly jumped for joy. "Then make yourself tidy," Grandfather said, pointing to a large tub full of water by the door. "Otherwise, the sun will laugh at you."

Heidi ran to the tub and began splashing and rubbing as hard as she could. Grandfather went inside the hut with Peter. He gave Peter some bread and cheese to put in the lunch bucket, and said, "The child is going with you. Take care she does not fall off the rocks."

Heidi now came running in. "Will the sun laugh at me now, Grandfather?" she asked seriously. She had scrubbed so hard she was as red as a lobster.

Grandfather laughed. "No, there's nothing for him to laugh at now. Go along."

Joyfully, Heidi ran for the mountain. The green slopes swarmed with flowers, and she ran on in front, picking whole handfuls of them. Soon she was out of sight. Peter could not see her anywhere.

"Where have you got to now, Heidi?" the boy called out somewhat crossly.

"I'm right here," called back a voice from somewhere close by.

"Come along now!" called Peter again. "You might fall off the rocks, and your grandfather gave me orders that you were not to do so. Besides, if you gather all the flowers today, there will be none left for tomorrow."

This last argument seemed to convince Heidi. She sprang up and ran to Peter with her apron full of flowers.

The goats began to act in a more orderly way, too. They could smell the plants growing on the higher slopes. Soon the pasture was reached, and the climb was at an end.

After Peter had placed the lunch bucket in a little hollow in the ground, he stretched out to take a nap. Heidi rolled her apron very carefully around the flowers and laid the small bundle beside the lunch bucket. She then sat down and looked around.

The valley lay far below, bathed in sunlight. All around was a great stillness, broken only by soft light puffs of wind that swayed the flowers. Heidi sat without moving. Peter had fallen asleep, and the goats were climbing among the bushes overhead.

So time went on. To Heidi, who had so often looked up at the mountains from the valley, they now seemed to have faces. They were looking down at her like old friends.

Suddenly she heard a loud harsh cry. Lifting her eyes, she saw a bird, larger than any she had ever seen. It was wheeling around in wide circles over her head.

"Peter! Wake up!" Heidi cried. "See that great bird there—look, look!"

Peter woke up then. Together, they watched the bird rise in the blue air till it disappeared behind the gray mountaintops.

"Where has it gone?" asked Heidi.

287

"Home, to its nest," said Peter.

"Is its home up there? Oh, how nice to be so high! Let's climb up there and see where the nest is," cried Heidi.

"No, no!" exclaimed Peter. "Why, even the goats can't climb that high. Besides, didn't your grandfather tell me you were not to fall off the rocks?"

All at once, Peter began to whistle and call in such a loud manner that Heidi could not think what was happening. The goats understood, for they came springing down the rocks till they were all grouped around him.

Peter took the lunch bucket from the hollow and placed the pieces of bread and cheese on the ground. Then he took a little bowl and milked some fresh milk into it from the white goat. He set the bowl of milk down beside the bread and the cheese.

"Leave off jumping about. It's time for dinner," he called to Heidi, who was romping about with the goats.

As they were eating, Heidi watched the goats frolicking about in the sun. "Tell me their names, Peter, will you?"

Peter knew these by heart, for, after all, he was a goatherd and had little else to carry about in his head.

There was the great Turk with his big horns, who was always wanting to butt the others. Only Greenfinch, the slender, nimble, little goat, was brave enough to face him. Then there was little White Snowflake, who bleated so sadly that Heidi had run several times to comfort her.

Just at this moment the pleading young cry was heard again. Heidi jumped up and put her arms around the little creature's neck. "What is it, little Snowflake?" she

asked. "Why do you cry as if you were in great trouble?"

Peter answered from where he was sitting, "She cries because her mother was sold in the village yesterday and will not be coming up the mountain any more."

"Oh, you poor little Snowflake!" exclaimed Heidi. "Do not cry. I shall come up here with you every day so you won't be lonely."

By this time, Heidi had decided that by far the handsomest and best-behaved goats were her grandfather's—Little Swan and Little Bear. They carried themselves with a certain pride and went their own way.

The goats were now beginning to climb the rocks again, each looking for the plants it liked best to eat. Little Swan and Little Bear clambered lightly up and never failed to find the best bushes. Heidi stood there, carefully watching all they did.

"Peter," she said to the boy, who had again stretched out on the ground. "The prettiest of all the goats are Grandfather's—Little Swan and Little Bear."

"I know they are," he said.

Just then Peter leaped to his feet and ran after the goats. Heidi followed him as fast as she could. He dashed toward that side of the mountain where the rocks fell to a great depth below. The curious Greenfinch had leaped to the very edge.

Peter was just in time. He threw himself down and grabbed one of her hind legs. The goat struggled so hard to get loose that Peter called Heidi to help him.

Quickly, Heidi gathered a bunch of sweet-smelling leaves and held them under the goat's nose. Greenfinch turned and began to eat the leaves out of Heidi's hand. Meanwhile, Peter got to his feet again. He took hold of the goat's collar and quietly led her back to the rest of the flock.

So the day crept on to its close. Now the sun was sinking behind the mountains. Heidi was again sitting on the ground, silently looking around her. A golden light lay on the grass and flowers, and the rocks above were beginning to shine.

All at once she sprang to her feet. "Peter! Everything is on fire! All the rocks are burning. Look! That high rock up there is red with flame! Stand up, Peter!"

"It is always like that," said Peter calmly, "but it is not really fire."

"What is it, then?" asked Heidi.

"It gets like that of itself."

"Look!" cried Heidi in fresh excitement, "now the mountains have all turned rose color. See that one covered with snow— beautiful crimson snow! And that one with the high pointed rocks? There are roses all over the rocks! Oh! Now they're turning gray. All the color has died away!"

Heidi sat down on the ground, looking as if the world were coming to an end.

"It will come again tomorrow," said Peter.

"Get up, we must go home now." He whistled to the goats, and they all started on their homeward way together.

"Will it come again tomorrow for sure?" asked Heidi as they climbed down.

"Yes, yes, for sure," Peter answered.

Heidi felt quite happy again and did not speak till they reached the hut. Grandfather was sitting under a fir tree in the yard, waiting for their return.

"Oh, Grandfather," Heidi cried even before she had come up to him, "it was so beautiful! The fire and the roses on the rocks and the blue and yellow flowers, and look what I have for you." Opening her apron she shook the flowers out at her grandfather's feet.

Oh, but how changed the flowers were! They looked like dry bits of hay.

"What's the matter with them?" exclaimed Heidi in shocked surprise. "They were not like that this morning."

"They like to stand out in the sun and not be shut up in an apron," said her grandfather with a twinkle in his eye.

Later, as Heidi sat on a high stool drinking milk, she gave Grandfather an account of the whole day. She asked many questions, and he answered them all.

Heidi liked best what he said about the fire on the mountains. He said, "When the sun says good night to the mountains, he throws his most beautiful colors over them. He does this so the mountains may not forget him before he comes again the next day."

Heidi could hardly wait for the next day. Then she would again climb up with Peter and the goats and watch the sun bid good night to the mountains.

THE COWARDLY LION

A great wind blew Dorothy and her dog, Toto, far from Kansas to the Land of Oz. Dorothy wanted to go home, but she didn't know the way. Then a good witch told her to follow the road to the Emerald City, where the Wizard of Oz would help her.

Dorothy started off alone, but the Tin Woodman and the Scarecrow joined her.

All this time Dorothy and her companions had been walking through the deep woods. The road was still paved with yellow bricks, but it was covered with dried branches and leaves. The walking was not at all good.

Now and then, there came a deep growl from some wild animal hidden in the trees. These growls made Dorothy's heart beat fast, for she didn't know what made them. Toto knew, though, and he walked close by Dorothy's side and did not bark in return.

"When will we be out of the forest?" Dorothy asked the Tin Woodman.

"I cannot tell," was the answer, "because I never have been to the Emerald City. My father was there once, and he said it was a long journey through dangerous country.

"I'm not afraid so long as I have my oil-can," the Woodman went on, "and nothing can hurt the Scarecrow. You, Dorothy, bear the mark of the good witch's kiss upon your forehead. That will protect you from harm."

"But Toto!" said the girl anxiously. "What will protect him?"

"We must protect him ourselves, if he is in danger," replied the Tin Woodman.

Just then there came a terrible roar from the forest. The next moment a great lion bounded into the road. With one blow of his

296

paw, he sent the Scarecrow spinning over and over to the edge of the road.

Then the Lion struck the Tin Woodman with his sharp claws. To the Lion's surprise, he made no impression on the tin, though the poor Woodman fell down and lay still.

Little Toto, now that he had an enemy to face, ran barking toward the Lion. The great beast opened his mouth to bite the dog. Then Dorothy, heedless of the danger, rushed forward and slapped the Lion on his nose!

"Don't you dare bite Toto!" she cried. "You ought to be ashamed of yourself, a big beast like you, to bite a little dog."

"I didn't bite him," said the Lion, rubbing his nose where she had hit him.

"No, but you tried," she retorted. "You are nothing but a big coward!"

"I know it," said the Lion, hanging his head in shame, "but how can I help it?"

"I don't know, I'm sure. To think of your striking a stuffed man, like my friend, the poor Scarecrow!"

"Is he stuffed?" asked the Lion in surprise. Then he watched Dorothy set the Scarecrow back on his feet and pat him into shape again.

"Of course, he's stuffed," replied Dorothy, who was still angry.

"That's why he went over so easily," said the Lion. "I was surprised to see him whirl around so. Is the other man, that I hit with my paw, stuffed, too?"

"No," said Dorothy, "he's made of tin." Then she helped the Woodman up again.

"That's why he nearly blunted my claws," said the Lion. "When my claws scratched against the tin, it made a cold shiver run down my back. What is the little animal?"

"He is my dog, Toto," answered Dorothy.

"Is he made of tin, or stuffed?"

"Neither. He's a—a—a meat dog."

"Oh! My, he's a curious animal, and so very small! No one would think of biting such a little thing except a coward like me," the Lion continued sadly.

"Just what makes you a coward?" asked Dorothy, looking at the great beast in wonder. He was as big as a small horse.

"It's a mystery," replied the Lion. "I suppose I was born that way. All the other animals in the forest expect me to be brave, for the Lion is everywhere thought to be the King of all the Beasts.

"If I roar loudly, every living thing is frightened, and runs away." The Lion sighed and then went on talking. "Of course, if the elephants and tigers and bears ever tried to fight me, I'd run away myself—I'm such a coward. Now, when they hear me roar they run, and I just let them go, naturally."

"But that isn't right. The King of Beasts shouldn't be a coward," said the Scarecrow in his husky voice.

"I know it," returned the Lion, wiping a

tear from his eye with the tip of his tail. "It is my great sorrow, and makes my life very unhappy. Still, whenever there is danger, my heart begins to beat fast."

"Perhaps you have heart disease," said the Tin Woodman. "You ought to be glad, for it proves you have a heart. Now, I have no heart, so I can't have heart disease."

"Perhaps," said the Lion thoughtfully, "if I had no heart I wouldn't be a coward."

"Have you brains?" asked the Scarecrow.

"I suppose so. I've never looked to see," replied the Lion.

"I'm going to the great Oz to ask him to give me some," remarked the Scarecrow, "for my head is stuffed with straw."

"And I am going to ask him to give me a new heart," said the Woodman.

"And I am going to ask him to send Toto and me back to Kansas," added Dorothy.

"Do you think Oz could give me courage?" asked the Cowardly Lion.

"Just as easily as he could give me some brains," said the Scarecrow.

"Or give me a heart," said the Woodman.

"Or send me back to Kansas," said Dorothy.

"Then, if you don't mind, I'll go with you," said the Lion, "for my life is simply unbearable without a bit of courage."

"You will be very welcome," said Dorothy, "for you will keep away other wild beasts. It seems to me they must be more cowardly than you, if they will allow you to scare them as easily as you do."

"They really are," said the Lion, "but that doesn't make me any braver. As long as I am a coward, I shall be unhappy."

Then the little company started on once more to the Emerald City. "We're off to see the Wizard," sang Dorothy, and the others joined in "—the wonderful Wizard of Oz."

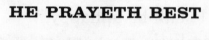

HE PRAYETH BEST

He prayeth best, who loveth best
All things both great and small;
For the dear God who loveth us,
He made and loveth all.

BE LIKE THE BIRD

Be like the bird, who
Halting in his flight
On limb too slight
Feels it give way beneath him,
Yet sings
Knowing he hath wings.

THE EMPEROR'S NEW CLOTHES

Many years ago there lived an Emperor who cared so much for fine clothes that he had a new coat for every hour of the day. He spent most of his time riding through the streets so that everyone might see how handsome his clothes were.

One day there came to the city two rogues, who set themselves up as weavers. The would-be weavers said they knew how to make the most wonderful cloth in the world. The cloth was very beautiful, they said, but it couldn't be seen by anyone who was either stupid or unfit for his office.

"I must have some clothes made from this cloth," thought the Emperor. "When I wear them I'll find out which men in my empire are not fit for their places. I'll know the clever men from the dunces. Those weavers must be brought to me at once."

So the rogues came to the palace, and the Emperor gave them a vast sum of money so that they might begin their work.

Quickly, the rogues set up two great looms. They called for the finest silk and the brightest gold thread, but these they put in their pockets. They pretended to work at the empty looms all day and far into the night.

Day after day, the Emperor could hear the rattling of the looms. He became very curious to see the wonderful clothes. So he decided to send someone to find out how the weavers were getting on. Still, he remembered that no one who was stupid or unfit for his office would be able to see the cloth.

"I'll send my faithful old Minister to the weavers," thought the Emperor. "He is a very clever man, and no one is more worthy of his office than he."

So the good old Minister went into the room where the two rogues sat working at the empty looms. He stared and stared, and opened his eyes as wide as he could.

"Mercy on us!" he thought. "I can't see a thing." He didn't say this aloud.

"Step a little nearer," said the rogues. "Isn't this a beautiful pattern? Aren't the colors wonderful?" The rogues pointed happily to the empty looms.

The poor old Minister put on his glasses and

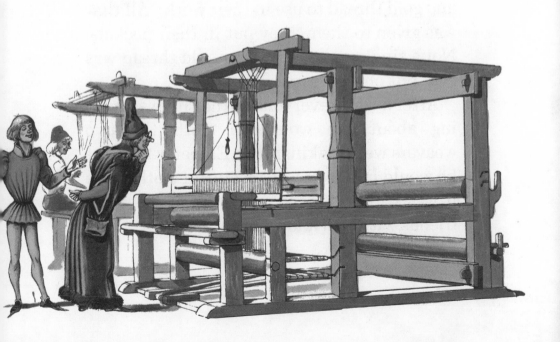

bent over the looms. He could see nothing, of course. There was nothing to see!

"Well, sir, what do you think of it?" asked one of the rogues.

The old Minister knew it would never do to say he couldn't see the stuff. "Oh, it's charming—beautiful," he said, peering through his glasses. "The colors are lovely and so is the pattern."

"We're glad, indeed, to hear you say so," said the rogues, and they went on talking about the cloth. They named the colors and described the pattern. The old Minister listened carefully, for he wished to repeat all that was said to the Emperor.

Soon the rogues began to ask for more silk and gold thread to use in their work. All that was given to them, they put in their pockets. Not a single strand of silk or gold thread was ever put on the looms.

After a while everyone in the city was talking about the wonderful cloth the two weavers were making. The Emperor thought he would like to see the beautiful cloth while it was still on the looms. So he took several friends with him and went to visit the rogues.

"What is this?" thought the Emperor when he saw the empty looms. "I see nothing at all. Am I not fit to be the Emperor? If that were known, I'd lose my empire."

Aloud he said, "Yes, yes, the cloth is very pretty. I am well pleased with it."

He smiled and nodded his head and stared at the empty looms. His friends, too, looked and looked, but saw no more than he did. Yet they all cried, "It is wonderful!" They asked the Emperor to wear a suit made from the new cloth in the great procession that was soon to take place.

As the day of the procession came nearer, the two rogues worked with might and main. They were up the whole of the night before, and they kept more than sixteen candles burning in their room.

Through the shining windows the people could see them hard at work. They took yards of nothing down from the empty looms. They made cuts in the air with big scissors. They sewed many stitches without any thread. At last they said, "The clothes are ready."

The Emperor then went in to put on his new suit. The rogues lifted their arms as if they were holding the clothes.

"See?" they said. "Here is the coat! Here is the cape! Here are the trousers! The cloth is as light as a spider's web. You may move as freely as if you had nothing on. That is the beauty of it."

"It's wonderful!" said the Emperor's friends. Yet all the time they saw nothing.

"Will your Majesty be pleased to take off your suit?" asked the rogues. "Then we will help you dress."

The Emperor took off his suit, and the rogues pretended to help him put on each new

garment. They wrapped him about, they buttoned, and they tied.

"How well his Majesty looks in the lovely new suit," said his friends. "What a becoming style! What beautiful colors!"

The Emperor turned round and round before a long mirror. He looked and looked, and nodded his head and smiled.

"I am ready," said the Emperor. He gave one last look in the mirror, as if he were again admiring his new finery.

The two men who were to carry the Emperor's train stooped down to the floor, as if picking up something. Then they held their hands high and moved forward.

The Emperor marched along, and all his officers marched behind him. The people in the streets gazed only at the Emperor, for they wanted to see his beautiful clothes.

"How handsome the Emperor's clothes are!" they all cried. "What a perfect fit! And such wonderful colors!"

No one would say he could see nothing, for that would have proved him very stupid and unfit for his office. No clothes of the Emperor ever had been so much admired.

"He has nothing on but his underwear," said a little child who saw the Emperor.

"Hush! Hush!" said the child's father, but the people who had heard the child's words began to whisper them to one another. "He had nothing on but his underwear."

Soon everyone was saying aloud, "He has nothing on but his underwear!"

The Emperor heard the people and shivered, for he knew they were telling the truth. He did not want to stop the procession, so he held himself stiffer than ever and marched on. Behind him, his officers carried the make-believe train.

THE BELL OF ATRI

In Italy there was once a little town by the name of Atri. The king had a great bell hung in the market place of the town. He had a roof built over the bell to shelter it from the sun and the rain.

Then he called the people of the town together and explained how the bell was to be used. "Whenever a wrong is done any man, he shall ring the great bell," said the king. "I have chosen a judge who will see that the wrong is made right again."

After that there were happy days in Atri, for the judge was a fair man who made right all the wrongs brought to his attention by the ringing of the bell.

In time, the rope wore away with much use and became frayed. Someone noticed this and mended the rope with a vine. The green leaves of the vine hung down to the ground.

Now it happened that a knight who had once loved to hunt lived in Atri. As a young man, he had loved his hounds and his horses. Since he had become old, he loved only one thing—his gold.

The knight sold his hounds and all of his horses but one. This horse was so old that no one would buy it. So the knight kept the old horse, but he did not take good care of it. He was too busy planning how to get more gold for himself.

At last he said, "What is the use of keeping this old horse that is eating his head off in my stable? Food is dear! Let him go feed upon the wayside."

The poor old horse was turned out into the street to find what grass he could. Day after day he wandered about, hungry and often cold. Stray dogs barked at him, and thorns tore his coat that had once been so silky.

On the very afternoon that someone had mended the bell rope with a vine, all the people in town were taking a nap. Suddenly they were roused by the sound of the great bell. The judge turned on his bed and listened. Then he rose, put on his robes, and hurried to the market place.

The bell was still ringing. "Ding-dong, ding-dong. Someone has been done a wrong, a wrong," it seemed to say.

When the judge reached the market place,

he saw neither a man nor a woman, but a poor hungry horse tugging at the green vine.

"Ah!" cried the judge. "This is the Knight of Atri's horse. He has met with a wrong, and he rings the bell as loudly as the people who have rung it before him."

From the streets and lanes the people of the town came running. They told the story of the poor horse in twenty ways, with much shaking of heads and fists.

At last the judge called the Knight of Atri. "And so my horse has roused you from your naps," he said. Then he tried to laugh, but the people did not join him.

"You have done your horse a wrong," they said, "and he rang the bell."

The knight grew angry. "I'll do as I please with my own horse," he cried.

Then the judge spoke. "It is the will of the king," he said, "that anyone who rings this bell shall have his wrong made right. When this horse was young, he served you well. Now that he is old, you must give him shelter in your stable and food and a good pasture, as well. He has earned them."

The knight was ashamed to think that he had treated the horse so badly. He promised to care for the horse and led it home.

When the king heard that a horse had rung the bell, he said, "I am well pleased. My bell helps not only men and women, but animals, too, who cannot tell of their wrongs. This horse has made the Bell of Atri famous for all time to come!"

The king was right, for the story of the Bell of Atri still lives, and will never die.

THE GREEDY MAN GETS HIS SHARE

Rama, King of Hansi, was a very kind man. He lived in a large palace and had a lovely garden, filled with apple, pear, and cherry trees. Pigeons, parrots, and peacocks roamed freely in the garden because no one was allowed to catch or hurt them.

The king had told his people to come to see him whenever they wished. Very few came, however, because of a certain soldier who stood guard at the palace gate.

Rama often asked the guard why more people did not come to the palace.

The guard always gave the same answer. "The people are busy with their work," he would say, "and do not have time to visit."

The truth was that a great many people came to the palace gate every day, but the guard stopped them. He wouldn't allow anyone inside the gate unless that person would give him some money.

A few rich men gave the greedy guard money, and he let them see the king. The poor people couldn't give him anything, so he always turned them away from the gate.

Now Rama had one child, a charming princess. He loved his daughter very much and gave her anything she wanted. Just before her tenth birthday, he asked her what special birthday gift she would like to have.

The princess had seen green-and-blue peacocks in the palace garden, but she had seen a picture of a white peacock in a storybook. She liked the picture and decided that she wanted a white peacock for her birthday.

White peacocks were very rare, and the king knew that it would be hard to find one. Since he didn't want to disappoint his daughter, he sent a message to all his people. The message said that King Rama wanted a white peacock. It also said that whoever brought such a rare bird to the palace would receive a fine, rich reward.

Many people searched, but no one could find a white peacock. Then, the day before the birthday of the princess, a poor woodcutter happened to see a pure white peacock in the forest. Quietly and carefully, the man moved close to the bird from behind and threw a big cloth over it. Then he tied the peacock's feet so that it could not get away and started for the palace.

He kept the bird covered, for he did not want anyone to see it. He was afraid that someone might steal it from him because of the reward that the king had promised.

The woodcutter never had been to the king's palace, and he knew nothing about the greedy guard. He found out, of course, as soon as he arrived at the gate.

"Halt!" said the guard. "Where do you think you are going? This is the palace of King Rama. You look like a beggar. What could you want with the king?"

The woodcutter said, "Please, Mr. Guard, I

317

know this is King Rama's palace. Nevertheless, I must go in. You see, I have something
in my bundle that will make the king happy."

When the guard asked what was in the
bundle, the woodcutter said he didn't wish to
tell. Then the guard said that unless he could
see what was in the bundle, the woodcutter
could not go through the gate.

Unwillingly, the woodcutter opened the
bundle. As soon as the guard saw the white
peacock, he knew that the woodcutter would
receive a rich reward for it.

"You must promise to give me half of the
reward you get from the king for this gift,"
said the greedy guard.

The woodcutter agreed to give the guard half of the reward and went on. When Rama saw the bird, he was delighted.

"Now, my good man," said the king to the woodcutter, "what reward do you want? I shall give you whatever you ask."

The woodcutter replied, "My King, I do not want money. The reward I want is fifty strokes on my bare back with a cane."

The king was amazed, but no matter how much he argued, the woodcutter wouldn't change his mind. At last the king called a soldier and said, "Please do as this man asks. Use the cane gently, though, for I do not want him to be hurt."

The soldier picked up a cane and began to beat the woodcutter on his bare back. He counted each stroke aloud. The woodcutter remained silent until the soldier had counted to twenty-five. Then he shouted, "Stop!"

Turning to the king, he said, "O King, the guard at your gate would not allow me to enter with the white peacock until I promised him half of the reward. I have now received my half. Please give the other half to him."

The king was amazed and angry to hear

that the guard he had trusted could have done such a thing. He sent for the guard and commanded the soldier to give the greedy man his share of the woodcutter's reward.

Afterward, the king said to the guard, "Now I know why so few people have come to see me. Leave my service at once."

The guard knew that his own greed had caused his downfall, and he went away. Then the king asked the woodcutter to be the new gateman at the palace. From that time on, the people of Hansi could come to see the good King Rama whenever they wished.

GLOSSARY OR LITTLE DICTIONARY

This glossary, or little dictionary, has been included to help you read the selections in this book. It includes the more difficult words in the book—the words that may cause you trouble in reading.

In finding out how to pronounce words, you will need to use diacritical marks and accent marks. The diacritical marks are used with the vowel letters to show how the vowels should be sounded. If you learn how to use these diacritical marks, you can easily tell how to pronounce words. The following table, or pronunciation key, shows you how to sound the different vowels.

ā as in lace	ē as in her	o͞o as in moon
ă as in map	ī as in ice	o͝o as in foot
ä as in arm	ĭ as in it	ū as in huge
â as in dare	ō as in note	ŭ as in cup
ē as in me	ŏ as in not	û as in urn
ĕ as in met	ô as in order	ü as in blue

Most words of more than one syllable have accent marks, telling which syllables should be accented in saying or pronouncing the words. Many longer words have two accent marks, a heavy mark to show which syllable should be accented strongly, and a light accent mark to show which syllable should be accented lightly.

Some of the syllables in words are unaccented. In saying the words, you almost pass over the syllables without noticing them. This mark (ə), called the schwa, is used in place of vowels to indicate unaccented syllables, as in place of the following:

a in arise	i in pencil	u in cactus
e in given	o in violet	

321

A

adobe (ə dō′ bǐ) : made of brick that is dried in the sun

adopted (ə dŏp′ tǐd) : took for one's own

afeared (ə fērd′) : afraid

Africa (ăf′ rə kə) : large continent south of Europe

airlock (âr′lŏk) : chamber in which a person is placed to make ready for any sudden great change in air pressure

alarm (ə lärm′) : sudden fear

amazement (ə māz′ mənt) : great or sudden surprise

andiron (ănd′ ī ərn) : one of a pair of iron supports for holding wood in a fireplace

annoyed (ə noid′) : bothered or disturbed; angered

antique (ăn tēk′) : something made long ago

argument (är′ gū mənt) : reason given for or against something

armor (är′ mər) : covering worn to protect the body in battle

arrant (ăr′ənt) : out-and-out

Australia (ôs trāl′ yə) : continent southeast of Asia, between the Indian Ocean and the Pacific Ocean

B

bachelor (băch′ ə lər) : man who has not married

batter (băt′ ər) : mixture of eggs, milk, flour, and other things, prepared for baking cookies, cakes, or gingerbread

Battle of Bunker Hill (băt′ əl əv Bŭngk′ ər hǐl) : battle fought early in the American Revolution near Bunker Hill in Boston, Massachusetts

beacon (bē′ kən) : light used as a warning or guiding signal

bellowing (bĕl′ ō ǐng) : roaring angrily

beret (bə rā′) : soft round cap

blast (blăst) : sudden and violent burst of gas from rear opening of a rocket

---

ā, lace; ă, map; ä, arm; à, dare; ē, me; ĕ, met; ē, her; ī, ice; ǐ, it; ō, note; ŏ, not; ô, order; ōo, moon; ŏo, foot; ū, huge; ŭ, cup; û, urn; ü, blue

blunted (blŭnt' ĭd) : made dull by use; not sharp

bodice (bŏd' ĭs) : close-fitting jacket, usually laced, worn by women and girls; sometimes a wide belt

boiler (boil' ər) : metal tank for making steam to drive an engine

booth (bōōth) : small, covered building with an open front where goods are sold at a fair or market

brass (brăs) : shiny yellowish metal used for making household goods or musical instruments

British (brĭt' ĭsh) : people of Great Britain and the British Commonwealth

bulb (bŭlb) : round underground bud from which certain plants grow, such as tulips or daffodils

button hook (bŭt' ən hŏŏk') : hook used to draw buttons through button holes

C

calico (kăl' ə kō) : cotton cloth with a decorative pattern printed on one side

canal (kə năl') : man-made waterway

canvas (kăn' vəs) : strong, heavy cloth used to make tents, sails, and wagontops

cape (kāp) : sleeveless outer garment that hangs loosely from the shoulders

capsule (kăp' səl) : small container, often containing medicine

career (kə rēr') : course of action through life or in a given field of work

carriage (kăr' ĭj) : vehicle with wheels in which people ride from place to place

chime (chīm) : set of bells or metal bars that play a tune when struck

clatter (klăt' ər) : noise, especially a confused mixture of noises, as on a street

---

ā, lace; ă, map; ä, arm; â, dare; ē, me; ĕ, met; ē̃, her; ī, ice; ĭ, it; ō, note; ŏ, not; ô, order; ōō, moon; ŏŏ, foot; ū, huge; ŭ, cup; û, urn; ü, blue

clearing (klēr′ ĭng) : piece of land from which trees and bushes have been removed

clodhopper (klŏd′ hŏp′ ər) : country bumpkin; plodding, heavy-footed fellow

clover (klō′ vər) : small plant with leaves of three parts and white, red, or purple flowers

coat of arms (kōt əv ärmz) : emblem shaped like a shield and bearing various meaningful designs, formerly worn by knights and nobles

coiled (koild) : wound round and round into a pile

colony (kŏl′ ə nĭ) : settlement made by a group of people who move to a new place or country

Continental Congress (kŏn′ tə něn′ təl kŏng′ grĭs) : group of men who represented the American Colonies and helped to run the country in the Revolutionary War

convince (kən vĭns′) : persuade; make someone believe

coonskin (kōōn′ skĭn) : skin of a raccoon, used as material for caps and other clothing

cornmeal dodger (kôrn′ mēl′ dŏj′ ər) : biscuit made of ground or crushed corn

cranberry (krăn′ běr′ ĭ) : sour red berry used for making jelly or sauce

cranked (krăngt) : started a motor with an arm or handle

crimson (krĭm′ zən) : deep red color

critter (krĭt′ ər) : dialect spelling of creature

crocodile (krŏk′ ə dīl) : animal with a long head, long body, long tail, four short legs, and a tough thick skin

crystal (krĭs′ təl) : clear mineral that looks like glass or ice

cuckoo clock (kōōk′ ōō klŏk) : clock with a small toy cuckoo that comes out to announce the time of day

---

ā, lace; ă, map; ä, arm; â, dare; ē, me; ĕ, met; ē, her; ī, ice; ĭ, it; ō, note; ŏ, not; ô, order; ōō, moon; ŏŏ, foot; ū, huge; ŭ, cup; û, urn; ü, blue

curiosity (kūr′ ĭ ŏs′ ə tĭ) : strong wish to know something

current (kûr′ ənt) : movement; flow of electricity or water in a certain direction

curtsy (kûrt′ sĭ) : bow made by lowering the body slightly and bending the knees

D

damage (dăm′ ĭj) : harm or injury

dappled (dăp′ əld) : covered with small spots

decent (dē′sənt) : proper; good enough

decks (dĕks) : decorates

definite (dĕf′ ə nĭt) : clear in meaning; possessing certain limits

depot (dē′ pō) : storehouse for freight

disappoint (dĭs ə point′) : fail to fulfil one's hope or wish

disease (də zēz′) : sickness

disgraced (dĭs grāst′) : out of favor; not respected

disturb (dĭs tûrb′) : trouble, worry; put out of order

dock (dŏk) : platform built into the water where ships may load or unload their cargoes

doily (doi′ lĭ) : small piece of lace or linen placed under a vase, bowl, or pictures

dragon (drăg′ ən) : huge legendary animal having wings, scales, claws, and able to breathe fire

drop-leaf (drŏp′ lēf′) : having leaves or sides that fold down when not in use, as a table

dunce (dŭns) : stupid person; child slow in learning to do things at home or school

E

Early Colonial (ẽr′ lĭ kə lō′ nĭ əl) : something made in the early days of the American colonies

electric (ē lĕk′ trĭk) : having to do with electricity or operated by electricity

---

ā, lace; ă, map; ä, arm; â, dare; ē, me; ĕ, met; ẽ, her; ī, ice; ĭ, it;
ō, note; ŏ, not; ô, order; ōō, moon; ŏŏ, foot; ū, huge; ŭ, cup; û, urn; ü, blue

emperor (ĕm′ pər ər) : ruler of an empire

empire (ĕm′ pīr) : group of nations headed by one ruler; a country ruled by an emperor

England (ĭng′ glənd) : largest part of Great Britain, south of Scotland, east of Wales

enormous (ĭ nôr′ məs) : very large

equally (ē′ kwəl ĭ) : same in amount, size, or number

evaporate (ĭ văp′ ə rāt) : change from liquid to vapor; disappear

experiment (ĕks pĕr′ ə mənt) : try to learn something by performing trials or tests

explode (ĕks plōd′) : blow up with a loud noise

eyelet (ī′ lĭt) : small hole in cloth or leather through which a cord or lace is inserted

F

fang (făng) : long, sharp, pointed tooth

fife (fīf) : small musical instrument like a flute, which makes a shrill sound when blown

fiord, fjord (fyôrd) : narrow arm or inlet of the sea with high rocky banks on either side

flabbergasted (flăb′ ĕr găst′ əd) : greatly surprised

flattery (flăt′ ər ĭ) : praise that is untrue or overdone

flinty (flĭnt′ ĭ) : like flint; made of flint

florist (flô′ rĭst) : person who sells flowers as a business

flurry (flûr′ ĭ) : sudden commotion or excitement

foreign (fôr′ ən) : having to do with a country not one's own

forelock (fôr′ lŏk) : lock of hair that grows just above the forehead

forlorn (fôr lôrn′) : sad; neglected; miserable

freight (frāt) : goods carried from place to place

ā, lace; ă, map; ä, arm; â, dare; ē, me; ĕ, met; ê, her; ī, ice; ĭ, it;
ō, note; ŏ, not; ô, order; ōō, moon; ŏŏ, foot; ū, huge; ŭ, cup; û, urn; ü, blue

French-Canadian (frĕnch kə nā′ dĭ ən) : having ancestors who were early French colonists of Canada

frolicking (frŏl′ ĭk ĭng) : playing about happily

G

gifted (gĭf′ tĭd) : having special ability

gingerly (jĭn′ jər lĭ) : with great care

glaring (glâr′ ĭng) : staring angrily

glistened (glĭs′ ənd) : sparkled; shone brightly

glittering (glĭt′ ər ĭng) : shining with a bright light; seeming to have shining bits in it

goatherd (gōt′ hĕrd′) : person who takes care of goats

gracias (grä′ sĭ əs) : Spanish word meaning "thank you"

granite (grăn′ ĭt) : kind of very hard stone

greed (grēd) : grasping desire for things

grooming (grōōm′ ĭng) : brushing and taking care of the appearance of an animal

guinea pig (gĭn′ ĭ pĭg) : small, short-eared, short-tailed animal somewhat like a large, harmless rat

gypsy (jĭp′ sĭ) : person belonging to a family or tribe of people who wander aimlessly about the world

H

haunted (hôn′ tĭd) : visited frequently by ghosts

headstrong (hĕd′ strông′) : hard to manage; foolishly determined to have one's own way

heedless (hēd′ lĭs) : thoughtless; careless

herring (hĕr′ ĭng) : kind of fish found in the northern Atlantic Ocean

hippopotamus (hĭp′ ə pŏt′ ə məs) : large plant-eating animal that lives in and near the rivers of central Africa

---

ā, lace; ă, map; ä, arm; â, dare; ē, me; ĕ, met; ē, her; ī, ice; ĭ, it;
ō, note; ŏ, not; ô, order; ōō, moon; ŏŏ, foot; ū, huge; ŭ, cup; û, urn; ü, blue

hoarse (hôrs) : having a deep, rough voice

Holland (hŏl′ ənd) : small country in Europe, also called the Netherlands

horror (hôr′ ər) : painful feeling of great fear

hustled (hŭs′ əld) : hurried

I

imitate (im′ ə tāt) : do something like; try to be like

impatient (ĭm pā′ shənt) : not willing to wait

impression (ĭm prĕsh′ ən) : mark made by pressing, stamping, or hitting

independence (ĭn′ dĭ pĕn′ dəns) : freedom from control by others

india-rubber (ĭn′ dĭ ə rŭb′ ər) : pure rubber; old name for rubber

Ireland (īr′ lənd) : one of the British Isles, divided into two parts: Irish Republic and Northern Ireland

J

jet plane (jĕt plān) : airplane driven forward by a stream of gas sent forcefully in the opposite direction

jumper (jŭmp′ ər) : loose jacket sometimes worn by workmen

K

kingdom (kĭng′ dəm) : country ruled by a king or emperor

knapsack (năp′ săk′) : leather or canvas bag carried on the back for clothes and other possessions

knight (nīt) : man with an honorary military rank in the Middle Ages, pledged to do good in the world

L

landlubber (lănd′ lŭb′ ər) : person who is not used to being on a ship

leash (lēsh) : strap which is used for leading or restraining an animal, as a dog

---

ā, lace; ă, map; ä, arm; â, dare; ē, me; ĕ, met; ē, her; ī, ice; ĭ, it;
ō, note; ŏ, not; ô, order; ōō, moon; ŏŏ, foot; ū, huge; ŭ, cup; û, urn; ü, blue

legend (lĕj′ ənd) : story handed down from the past, which many people once believed

lobster (lŏb′ stər) : sea animal with eight legs and two big front claws

loom (lo͞om) : machine used for weaving cloth

lunged (lŭnjd) : moved suddenly; leaped forward

M

magnet (măg′ nĭt) : piece of iron that pulls certain metal objects toward it

magnifying glass (măg′ nə fī ĭng glăs) : glass that makes objects seem larger than they really are

mane (mān) : heavy hair on the back of the neck of an animal, such as a lion or horse

mantle (măn′ təl) : anything that covers or surrounds, as a cloak

marketed (mär′ kĭt ĭd) : sold to someone in a market

marsh (märsh) : swamp

Middle West (mĭd′ əl wĕst) : central part of the United States between the Appalachian Mountains and the Rocky Mountains and north of the Ohio River and the southern boundaries of Missouri and Kansas

miniature (mĭn′ ĭ ə tər) : small example or copy of a large object

minister (mĭn′ ĭs tər) : head of a department of government in certain foreign countries

miracle (mĭr′ ə kəl) : something wonderful that happens yet cannot be explained

mused (mūzd) : thought

museum (mū zē əm) : place in which articles of scientific, artistic, or historical interest and importance are kept

N

national (năsh′ ən əl) : belonging to an entire country

ā, lace; ă, map; ä, arm; â, dare; ē, me; ĕ, met; ē, her; ī, ice; ĭ, it;
ō, note; ŏ, not; ô, order; o͞o, moon; o͝o, foot; ū, huge; ŭ, cup; û, urn; ü, blue

New Amsterdam (nū ăm′ stər dăm) : early Dutch name for New York City

nightingale (nīt′ ən gāl) : small European bird with a beautiful song

nimble (nĭm′ bəl) : light and quick in movement

notion (nō′ shən) : idea ; thought

O

official (ə fĭsh′ əl) : having government approval ; a government representative

oiler (oil′ ər) : ship that carries a cargo of oil

opossum (ə pŏs′ əm) : small grayish animal with coarse fur and a ratlike tail

oxygen (ŏk′ sə jən) : odorless, colorless gas that forms part of the air, water, and many other things in nature

P

papoose (pă pōos′) : Indian word for baby

particularly (pər tĭk′ ū lər lĭ) : belonging to a special time, thing, place, or person ; especially

partner (pärt′ nər) : person with whom one shares something, as the profits and losses of a business

pattern (păt′ ərn) : arrangement of forms or colors

peacock (pē′ kŏk′) : large bird with a beautiful tail that it can spread out like a fan

Philadelphia (fĭl′ ə dĕl′ fĭ ə) : city in Pennsylvania

pigtail (pĭg′ tāl) : long braid of hair hanging down from the back of the head

plastic (plăs′ tĭk) : material or substance that can be molded into shape

poison (poi′ zən) : anything dangerous to life or health

pranced (prănst) : danced or moved about on the hind legs

pretend (prĭ tĕnd′) : make believe that something is true

ā, lace; ă, map; ä, arm; â, dare; ē, me; ĕ, met; ē, her; ī, ice; ĭ, it;
ō, note; ŏ, not; ô, order; ōō, moon; ŏŏ, foot; ū, huge; ŭ, cup; û, urn; ü, blue

procession (prə sĕsh′ ən) : group of people moving forward together as in a parade

protein (prō′tə ĭn or prō′ tēn) : important cell-building substance in foods

puppet (pŭp′ ĭt) : small figure made to perform by use of strings or the hands

Q

quaint (kwānt) : pleasingly or amusingly strange

Quebec (kwĭ bĕk′) : province in Canada; capital of the province of Quebec

quince (kwĭns) : yellowish fruit used in making preserves

R

rajah (rä′ jä) : king or ruler in India and other Far Eastern countries

Rattlesnake Flag (răt′ əl snāk flăg) : flag used by some of the colonies during the Revolutionary War

recipe (rĕs′ ə pē) : directions for cooking or preparing a food of some kind

regular (rĕg′ ū lər) : steady; fixed by rule or law

relative (rĕl′ ə tĭv) : member of a person's own family, as mother, father, sister, brother, cousin, or aunt

retorted (rĭ tôrt′ əd) : replied sharply

ridge (rĭj) : long narrow hill

rogue (rōg) : dishonest, bad, tricky person

rollicking (rŏl′ ĭk ĭng) : lively and jolly

rubbish (rŭb′ ĭsh) : worthless things; trash

ruffled (rŭf′ əld) : gathered along one edge of something as a strip of cloth

S

sage (sāj) : wise

sailcloth (sāl′ klôth) : heavy, tightly woven cloth used in making sails

---

ā, lace; ă, map; ä, arm; â, dare; ē, me; ĕ, met; ē, her; ī, ice; ĭ, it;
ō, note; ŏ, not; ô, order; o͞o, moon; o͝o, foot; ū, huge; ŭ, cup; û, urn; ü, blue

schooner (skoon′ ər) : ship with two or more masts rigged with fore-and-aft sails

Scituate Bay (sĭt′ ū āt bā′) : small body of water almost surrounded by land in the state of Massachusetts

scroll (skrōl) : roll of paper with writing on it; design drawn or carved to look like a roll of paper

scurry (skûr′ ĭ) : hurry; run rapidly; scamper

selection (sĭ lĕk′ shən) : something chosen

shafts (shăfts) : wooden poles between which animals are hitched to pull a carriage

shuttle (shŭt′ təl) : small instrument used in weaving to pass a thread from one side of a loom to the other

siesta (sĭ ĕs′ tə) : Spanish word meaning "afternoon nap"

silversmith (sĭl′ vər smĭth′) : person who makes things from silver

skeleton (skĕl′ ə tən) : framework; bones of the body in their regular positions

slab (slăb) : broad flat piece of wood, stone, or meat

sleek (slēk) : smooth and glossy

slicker (slĭk′ ər) : long, loose raincoat

snail (snāl) : small, soft, slow-moving animal; person who moves slowly and lazily

snuffling (snŭf′ lĭng) : breathing loudly through the nose, as from a cold or crying

sourdough (sour′ dō′) : prospector in the western United States, Canada, and Alaska

spindle (spĭn′ dəl) : rod or pin on which something turns

splint (splĭnt) : strip of wood or metal to keep a broken bone in place

spyglass (spī′ glăs′) : small telescope that makes distant objects look larger and nearer

squishy (skwĭsh′ ĭ) : soft and easily crushed; squashy

ā, lace; ă, map; ä, arm; â, dare; ē, me; ĕ, met; ē, her; ī, ice; ĭ, it; ō, note; ŏ, not; ô, order; o͞o, moon; o͝o, foot; ū, huge; ŭ, cup; û, urn; ü, blue

T

tack (tăk) : sail or move in a zigzag course

talent (tăl′ ənt) : ability to perform or do something

temperate (tĕm′ pər ĭt) : neither very hot nor very cold ; moderate

thorns (thôrnz) : sharp pointed growths on a plant

tide (tīd) : rise and fall of the ocean every twelve hours

tiled (tīld) : covered with thin pieces of baked clay

tinder box (tĭn′ dər bŏks) : box for holding flint and steel and quick-burning materials for starting a fire

torrid (tôr′ ĭd) : very hot

tractor (trăk′ tər) : engine mounted on wheels for pulling plows, wagons, and other kinds of vehicles

tramp steamer (trămp stēm′ ər) : steamship that has no regular route but goes to any port along the way

trespassing (trĕs′ pəs ĭng) : going about on someone's property without permission

trial (trī′ əl) : act of trying or testing something

trolley (trŏl′ ĭ) : streetcar run by electricity coming from overhead wires

trundle-bed (trŭn′ dəl bĕd′) : small bed that slides or rolls under a large bed

turban (tûr′ bən) : headdress made by winding a scarf around the head

Turkey (tûr′ kĭ) : country in western Asia and southeastern Europe

tweak (twēk) : quick pull or twist

twine (twīn) : heavy string made by twisting two or more strands together

U

unbearable (ŭn bĕr′ ə bəl) : impossible to endure something, as agony or pain

---

ā, lace; ă, map; ä, arm; â, dare; ē, me; ĕ, met; ē, her; ī, ice; ĭ, it; ō, note; ŏ, not; ô, order; ōō, moon; ŏŏ, foot; ū, huge; ŭ, cup; û, urn; ü, blue

unbelievable (ŭn bē lēv′ ə bəl) : impossible to accept something as the truth

underbrush (ŭn′ dər brŭsh′) : heavy growth of small trees and bushes under tall trees in a woods or jungle

Union (ūn′ yən) : the United States of America

United States Congress (ū nīt′ ĭd stāts kông′ grĭs) : law-making body, made up of the Senate and the House of Representatives

V

vapor (vā′ pər) : tiny drops of water rising into the air

venison (vĕn′ ə zən) : meat of a deer

ventriloquist (vĕn trĭl′ ə kwĭst) : person who can make his voice seem to come from another source

vibrating (vī brāt′ ĭng) : quivering; moving rapidly back and forth or to and fro

W

wary (wâr′ ĭ) : cautious; afraid

wharf (hwôrf) : platform built along a shore or out over the water where ships load or unload their cargoes

wheezed (hwĕzd) : breathed with a whistling sound

whimpering (hwĭm′ pər ĭng) : crying like a sick dog or child

whinnied (hwĭn′ ĭd) : made a sound like a horse

white-washed (hwīt′ wôsht′) : painted with a liquid whitening made of lime and water

whittle (hwīt′ təl) : carve or shape with a knife

widow (wĭd′ ō) : woman who no longer has a husband

Y

yam (yăm) : kind of sweet potato

yore (yôr) : long ago

Yukon (yū′ kŏn) : territory in Canada; a river in Alaska and Canada

---

ā, lace; ă, map; ä, arm; â, dare; ē, me; ĕ, met; ẽ, her; ī, ice; ĭ, it; ō, note; ŏ, not; ô, order; o͞o, moon; o͝o, foot; ū, huge; ŭ, cup; û, urn; ü, blue

ACKNOWLEDGMENTS

Grateful credit is given to the following authors and publishers for permission to use copyrighted materials, and in a few cases honorary mention is made of authors whose works are now in the public domain:

The Bobbs-Merrill Company, Inc., for "Out of the World" from *Why the Chimes Rang and Other Stories* by Raymond MacDonald Alden, for "The Cowardly Lion" from *The Wizard of Oz* by L. Frank Baum, for "The Floogles Have Their Picture Taken" from *The Funny Fixes of the Floogle Family* by Gertrude Crampton, for "Old Brass and Iron" from *The Good Ship Spider Queen* by Eda and Richard Crist, for "Extremes" from *Joyful Poems for Children* by James Whitcomb Riley, and for "Ben's Great Experiment" from *Ben Franklin: Printer's Boy* by Augusta Stevenson; James T. Brady for "The Rajah's Secret" which appeared in *Jack and Jill*, reprinted by special permission from *Jack and Jill*, copyright 1959, The Curtis Publishing Company; Nora Burglon for "The Dragon Chair" which appeared originally in *Children's Playmate; Child Life* for "Monsieur Clop-Clop" by Nicolete Meredith Stack; Child Training Association, Inc., for "Golden Amak" and "Why Monkeys Scream at Crocodiles" by Willis Lindquist, and for "Amigo, My Burro" by Ina May Moore, all of which appeared in *Children's Activities*, used by permission of the publishers; George Cooper for "The Wonderful Weaver"; Harriet Evatt for "The Beaded Moccasin" from *The Snow Owl's Secret*, published by The Bobbs-Merrill Company, Inc.; Eugene Field for "Wynken, Blynken and Nod" from *Poems of Childhood*, Charles Scribner's Sons (1904); Fred Abbe Franzeim for "The Lighthouse Bell" which appeared in *Jack and Jill*, reprinted by special permission from *Jack and Jill*, copyright 1952, The Curtis Publishing Company; D. C. Heath and Company for "A Pioneer Housewarming" from *Adventuring with Pioneers* by Mary Browning, copyright 1949, used by permission of the publisher; Marion Holland for "Fats Takes the Cake" which appeared in *Story Parade;* Helen L. Howard for "The Angel Chimes" which appeared in *Child Life;* Victor Hugo for "Be Like the Bird"; Flora Gregg Iliff for "The Popcorn That Didn't Pop"; Humphrey Johnson for "First Child on Mars" which appeared in *Jack and Jill*, reprinted by special permission from *Jack and Jill*, copyright 1955, The Curtis Publishing Company; Marian King for "Betje's Tulip" which appeared in *American Junior Red Cross News*, and for "The Newcomer" which appeared in *Children's Activities;* S. K. Kirpalani for "The Greedy Man Gets His Share" which appeared in *Jack and Jill*, reprinted by special permission from *Jack and Jill*, copyright 1955, The Curtis Publishing Company; Don Lang for "Jenny and Her Pets" which appeared in *Story Parade;* Edward Lear for "The Owl and the Pussy Cat" from *Complete Book of Nonsense Rhymes;* Lee Priestley for "The Flying Gingerbread" which appeared in *Child Life;* Random House, Inc., for "Some of My Father's Adventures" from *My Father's Dragon* by Ruth Stiles Gannett; Abraham Segal for "The Mighty Candle" which appeared in *Jack and Jill*, reprinted by special permission from *Jack and Jill*, copyright 1954, The Curtis Publishing Company; Johanna Spyri for "Heidi's First Adventure" from *Heidi;* Robert Louis Stevenson for

"My Shadow" from *Child's Garden of Verses;* Story Parade, Inc., for "Lisa's Song" by Ruth Kennell, copyright 1941, and for "The Left-Over Hat" by Charles Williams, copyright 1953, both copyrighted by Story Parade, Inc., reprinted and adapted by special permission; William Makepeace Thackeray for "A Tragic Tale"; Claire Trask for "How Baby Animals Ride" which appeared under the title "Baby Animals Take a Ride" in *Jack and Jill,* reprinted by special permission from *Jack and Jill,* copyright 1954, The Curtis Publishing Company; Lucille Wallower for "The Legend of Betsy Ross" which appeared in *Jack and Jill,* reprinted by special permission from *Jack and Jill,* copyright 1954, The Curtis Publishing Company.

Appreciative credit is given C. B. Ulery, Managing Editor, and Elfrieda L. Schmidt, Associate Editor, for editorial guidance in the selection and presentation of the content of the volume.

Further credit is given William C. Heckler, Art Director, for his effective creative efforts in directing the preparation of art materials for the volume, and to the following artists who created the artwork found on the page numbers accompanying their names: Joseph Giordano, Cover; Jackie Lacy, end papers and page 6; Aliki, pages 1, 4, 5, 7, 55, 99, 139, 179, 217, and 265; Vincent Malta, pages 2, 3, 42, 43, and 148; Bonnie and Bill Rutherford, pages 8 through 14, and pages 49 through 54; Seymour Fleishman, pages 15 through 23; Bruno Frost, page 24, pages 44 through 48, and page 283; E. Joseph Dreany, pages 25 through 33; Audrey Walters, pages 34 through 41; Al Fiorentino, pages 56 through 63, pages 108 through 115, pages 180 through 182, pages 237 through 243, pages 253 through 263, and pages 266 through 275; Fritz Kredel, pages 64 through 72, pages 80 through 87, pages 276 through 282, and pages 303 through 310; Leslie Goldstein, pages 73 through 79, pages 88 through 98, and pages 133 through 138; Norman Kenyon, pages 100 through 107, pages 192 through 195, and pages 227 through 235; Herbert Danska, pages 116, 209, 264, and 302; Samuel Dion, pages 117 through 125, pages 183 through 191, and page 236; Isabel Dawson, pages 126 through 132, pages 198 through 202, and pages 218 through 226; Sari, pages 140 through 147, pages 166 and 167, and pages 174 through 178; Charles Clement, pages 149 through 159, pages 203 through 208, and pages 244 through 252; Stan Fraydas, pages 160 through 165, and pages 210 through 216; Maurice Rawson, pages 168 through 173, and pages 311 through 320; Jon Nielson, pages 196 and 197, and pages 284 through 294; Jean Macdonald Porter, pages 295 through 301.